Abou

Gabriel Hemery is a tree-~~~ ~~~~~~~~~ ~~ author.
While researching for his ~~~~~~ ~~iversity of Oxford), he
led an expedition to the mountains of Kyrgyzstan, collecting
walnut seeds from its threatened walnut-fruit forests. He
has since planted tens of thousands of trees in plantations
and forestry trials across Britain, and created a new research
woodland named Paradise Wood. He became the first full-
time employee of the Botanical Society of Britain & Ireland
before returning to forestry. In 2009, Gabriel co-founded
the Sylva Foundation, an environmental charity, where he
has since served as its chief executive. He is also a trustee
of an arboreal charity, Fund4Trees, and has acted as advisor
for a number of organisations, including the Forestry
Commission and the Woodland Trust. His first book, *The
New Sylva* (Bloomsbury Publishing, 2014), was widely
acclaimed, and he has since focused on writing fiction. He
writes a popular tree and forestry blog, which also features
news about his books and photography. This can be
explored at www.gabrielhemery.com.

@gabrielhemery

Green Gold

Green Gold

The Epic True Story of Victorian
Plant Hunter John Jeffrey

Gabriel Hemery

unbound

This edition first published in 2019

Unbound
6th Floor Mutual House, 70 Conduit Street, London W1S 2GF
www.unbound.com

This is a work of fiction. Some of its form and contents closely follow
known historical records, and these are clearly marked. Otherwise,
except for those already in the public domain, all names, characters,
businesses, events and incidents are the products of the author's
imagination, and any resemblance to reality is purely coincidental.

ISBN (eBook): 978-1-78965-024-2
ISBN (Paperback): 978-1-78965-023-5

Cover design by Mecob

Printed and bound in Great Britain by Clays Ltd, Elcograf S.p.A.

To my wife, Jane

With grateful thanks to Jonathan Drori and Forest Holidays Ltd for helping to make this book happen.

NOTHING GOLD CAN STAY

Nature's first green is gold,
Her hardest hue to hold.
Her early leaf's a flower;
But only so an hour.
Then leaf subsides to leaf.
So Eden sank to grief,
So dawn goes down to day.
Nothing gold can stay.

Robert Frost (1874–1963)

Contents

Super Patrons

Andy Smith
Henry Studholme
Elizabeth Turner
Joan Walker
Karen Walton
Norman & April Weiss
Andrew Wilkinson
Chris Wright

Author's Note

Many of the events in this biographical fiction actually occurred, while all are feasible. Historical evidence partly records an extraordinary, yet little known, true story of a plant hunter named John Jeffrey, who in 1850 was despatched by a wealthy group of British investors to North America in search of valuable plants. There were high hopes that this young man would follow in the footsteps of earlier illustrious collectors – among them David Douglas, Scottish botanist and namesake of the Douglas-fir – yet the odds were stacked against him. Much of the territory he travelled through had been explored already by other botanists, while his expedition happened to collide head-on with the Gold Rush as it spread northwards from California.

Insights into the planning and activities undertaken by the expedition's investors are recorded in the minute book of the Oregon Botanical Association. It is held in the archives of the Royal Botanic Garden Edinburgh, along with the few letters sent home by John Jeffrey, and a catalogue of others written between the expedition's subscribers. Short handwritten labels attached to the plant and insect specimens he sent home to Scotland often included details of latitude or altitude, and sometimes a place name. Together, this evidence provides tantalising, if incomplete, insights into the places he visited, the distances he travelled and his professional accomplishments. Yet the full story of John Jeffrey's expedition, including his personal challenges and conquests, together with his emotional journey, would have been captured in his expedition journals. He was formally contracted to compile a record in these journals, in duplicate no less, but despite repeated reminders from his employers, they never materialised.

Green Gold provides these missing journal entries through fiction, interwoven with a selection of the most significant historical evidence. To help those with an interest in history separate fact from fiction, sections marked with '✝' denote that a historical record is quoted. Some of these have been altered, but only ever to a minor extent, to improve readability. Where such notation is absent, it should be presumed that fiction rules, yet I hope readers may be surprised – should they later look into any historical character, language, place, business or plant – to discover further truths within the fiction.

Gabriel Hemery
December 2018

ORIGINATION

BIRTH, EXISTENCE AND BEGINNING

Arnold Arboretum, Boston, 3 September, present day

Professor Benedict Freeman opened the door for Helen and they entered the grove of archived plants together, their footsteps echoing from the boards cut by long-dead foresters. The heavy cedar door creaked shut behind them as they made their way across the main reading room. In a clearing at its centre, a highly polished table stood alone, startled by the bright autumnal sunlight streaming through three high-arched windows. The furniture's patina of sunburst and fiddleback veneer glowed underneath untidy piles of readers' notes and files.

At the edge of the room, panicles of small tables stemmed from the windows, each sharing an eye-catching view over the golden arboretum beyond. At the central cluster, two women conversed enthusiastically. The smaller of the pair blossomed in a bold floral dress. Her tall companion shrank under a pair of smart tailored trousers. Judging by their lack of uniform, Helen reckoned the unlikely pair must be volunteers. They stooped over a large portfolio, open to show a lifelike botanical drawing. Its vivid hand-coloured features were a dazzling reflection of the faded and fragile pressed plant mounted on the loose page next to it. Collected by a botanist long ago, the herbarium specimen's slender brown stem, delicate flowerhead and withered leaves were held in place with tidy stitches, made delicately through the heavy mounting card. Its lifeless form captured forever a discovery, a geography and a taxonomy.

'Hey, Ben, take a look at this,' said the floral woman, holding out a hand lens. 'Oh, I'm so sorry, I didn't realise you had company!' she added, seemingly noticing Helen standing beside him for the first time.

The professor registered Helen's look of surprise. 'We're very informal here. After all, we care about plants more than people! You should call me Ben, too.'

Turning his attention to the two volunteers, Ben

introduced Helen as the new intern. She was amazed to learn that the pair had 62 years of combined volunteering time between them. Ben's easy-going manner belied his botanical prowess, and their conversation soon moved on to why the anthers seemed longer in the colour plate than the herbarium specimen.

Helen's attention drifted. She noticed how every vertical surface of the room was covered with shelves that stretched from floor to ceiling, all of them laden with books. Many appeared to be of great vintage, with handsome leather spines and raised bands. Drifting away from the other three, she browsed dreamily along a set of shelves, running an index finger over the books' spines, tracing ridges and embossed lettering, imagining the generations of hands that had studied at the arboretum.

'Sorry, Helen,' interrupted the professor, catching up with her, his long legs making quick work of her dreamy peramble. 'It's impossible to ignore a botanical query like that. I'm stuck behind my computer too much these days.'

He must find time to exercise, though, thought Helen. *A cyclist, perhaps. So many other men his age have a paunch.* His eyes smiled down on her behind thin-framed glasses, which he pushed up his narrow nose.

They left the reading room together, walking in single file along one of the many narrow corridors leading from the back wall. Books and journals seemed to stretch to infinity, crowding in on both sides. At its end they halted in front of another wooden door.

'So, this is the room we've used to store the few remaining archival boxes of miscellaneous material.' Finding the key among a large bunch on a chain fixed to his trouser waist, Ben opened the heavy door.

As they entered, Helen noticed a brass fingerplate labelled with the name of its wood: 'American White Oak, *Quercus alba*'. She had expected a small store cupboard. The door opened instead on to a huge echoing space, measuring at least the same size again as the main reading room, yet it couldn't have contrasted more: bare magnolia walls, grey industrial epoxy floor and a lack of natural light lent it a soulless quality. Plastic archival storage crates covered most of the floor, the type with folding crenulated lids, allowing one to be stored on top of another. The boxes sat three-high in rows, forming a grey maze around the room.

'Now, don't be dismayed,' said the professor, seemingly reading her mind. 'I realise this must look daunting, but we always make sure interns experience plenty of variety. We thought working through some of these materials would be a perfect task when we're too short-staffed to supervise you in the field, like we are today, or when the weather's foul. Essentially, everything in here has been removed from long-term storage elsewhere – including various cellars, cupboards and storerooms – from right across the whole site. Nothing has been sorted through yet.'

'So where do I begin?'

'I suggest you start there,' he said, pointing to the far corner. 'We need to clear that area first, as these boxes are almost blocking access to the fire door. If you can simply sort contents into these different categories.' He handed her a notebook and pen, together with a crumpled list from the pocket of his linen jacket. 'I'll leave you to it, then. One of us will check back in an hour or so.'

Helen stood alone in the bleak room, surrounded by countless grey boxes, the hum of the overhead strip lights supplanting Ben's fading footsteps. *What am I doing here?* she wondered. She knew the answer well enough, really; it was a dream internship, one she'd had to work hard for, one she'd competed against more than 200 other students to win. It was worth her making every possible effort over the next six months.

Of the three crates in the corner, the first two were heavy, but easy enough to move further into the room where the light was a little better. The last one she couldn't budge, and so fate decided this would be the first box she explored. There seemed to be no order or logic to its contents; sheaves of handwritten notes intermingled with heavy books and journals, and even some beautiful hand-coloured illustrations of a purple iris showing its flower, details of its reproductive parts and its tuberous roots.

Helen set about sorting the items according to the categories the professor had provided, trying not to become overly distracted by the myriad interesting contents. Nearing the bottom of the crate, her hand fell upon a worn leather notebook, which on closer inspection she realised was bundled with several others, each tied shut with a long leather lace. The outer covers were worn and deeply stained, their margins frayed and tattered. Tucked under the laces were one or two folded sheets of paper that looked to be letters.

Untying one of the laces, she gingerly lifted the corner of the uppermost notebook. Bold loops of thin ink writing bounded across the page. She spotted a date that caused her to hold her breath: 1852. She'd never held something genuinely that old before. Curiosity overcame her, so she untied the ribbon fully and began to read.

Journal: Shasta Valley, California, 25 October 1852

I remember there was an unusually big sky that evening, and it was lonely of clouds – surely forewarning a sharp night. I raised a modest fire and added an extra layer of springy branches under my bedroll as a spectacular red sun descended between two giant boulders before me. Thus prepared I drifted to sleep, lying with some satisfaction beneath the canopy of another fine specimen of the magnificent new pine I had discovered days before (No. 731). A myriad stars flickered between the long needles on its gently swaying branches. I was reminded of Humboldt's analogy – of the blooming, fecundity and withering of stars and planets – and the form of the great garden of the universe which now lay open before me. God had revealed his infinite mysteries.

Sometime later, while wrapped tightly in a meagre HBC blanket, my hat drawn deep down over my head, such was the cold, I was woken by a great weight upon my chest. It has been more than one month since I last enjoyed close human comfort, and I was confused, before becoming immediately alert.

Yet, before I could much react, a terrible pain lanced my cheek, and I found my face to be held in a foul stinking vice. Despite finding myself quite blind, and with one arm caught under my blanket, with the other I managed to strike out. My bare hand encountered solid fur-clad muscle. So short was the coat of my foe, there was no handhold. I thought then that I was confronted, not by a grizzly, but most likely a mountain lion. I raised my legs to grapple with its body and rolled over to one side. I felt the flesh on my face tear open even as I felt for my gun. With the stock I aimed a blow blindly at its body and, on making satisfying contact, felt its jaws loosen. Yet still it did not retreat, its claws holding fast to my body. I fought viciously, with every limb and ounce of my strength, for what seemed many minutes, but must have been mere seconds, before it fled. By the time I had torn the remains of the hat off my head, I managed to glimpse only its long tail disappearing between the same two boulders between which the sun had earlier retreated. Yet there it paused to turn and stare. I feared for a moment it was to return, its unblinking eyes reflecting two startling full moons, yet it evidently decided that discretion was the better part of valour. With a turn of its head it was eclipsed by the night.

I immediately sought to rekindle the fire, which had faded to a pitiful glow. With my knife now permanently in one hand, which trembled terribly and quite without control, I heated water to tend to my face and other injuries. I slept for none of the remainder of the night, gripped, I admit, by terror, and suffering a most fearsome throbbing pain.

Naturally, I have no glass with me, so I was obliged to wait until the sun had risen before I could inspect my face on the surface of a pool in the creek. Being without the excitement of a fight to mask the pain, applying the crude stitches to my cheek hurt more than the beast's canines.

After attending to my wounds I believe that I became quite delirious. I woke many times to find myself surprised that it was day rather than night, or vice versa. My body was often drenched with sweat and I found myself shivering, even at noon when the sun was at its zenith. My fire, however, I kept burning day and night, even though the usually simple act of gathering kindling and logs was a great burden on account of the pain.

I write now, I believe, some two days after the attack. It is unusual for me to stay more than one night in the same place, but I have felt little able to do much more than rest and attend to the fire. While my symptoms were at their height, I experienced vivid and hallucinatory dreams. In many of these I found myself with Prof Woody, and other noble gentlemen, among extraordinary variations of the Edinburgh gardens. What would they think now of my sorry situation? If they could witness my immediate circumstances they would surely experience a similar sense of bewilderment, yet their vision would be no dream. I am a battered man, with a grizzly face, which surely masks completely the youth they despatched with such optimism but two years ago.

Evening

I recall Mr Anderson explaining the habits of the various beasts which might prove a threat to us. I have encountered many bears, both black and grizzly, during my travels thus far, and shot more than I can now remember. In fact, meetings are commonplace with these giants, and it is second nature to take measures to counter their curiosity when establishing an encampment. Yet I can recall seeing only two mountain lions in all my time traversing this vast country (the last one about one month past). On both of these occasions, they have been some distance away. I was well informed that a mountain lion will only rarely attack a man – a child being much more common fare – unless it is surprised, or if that man is a coward who presents a fleeing back. I will remember to inform my old guide of these experiences, if we are fortunate enough to meet again.

Earlier, I followed the path that the animal took between the boulders, and just beyond them, along the banks of the stream in the soft mud among its rushes, I found several footprints. Each was the size of the back of my hand. The rear of the main pads had three lobes, a feature I have not seen before. It may confirm my suspicion as to the beast's identity.

I have determined that I will start back northwards tomorrow, to find company as soon as possible in case my wounds fester, although I now feel a little more myself. The snow-clad peak of Mount Shasta exerts a dominant presence in this place, its foothills providing fertile hunting grounds for the botanist. Before me tall pines, all of the same new species that I found these days past, grow between massive boulders, extending without interruption down the valley and far into the distance. This land is a paradise so rich it would see the same gentlemen emptying their purses to secure more collectors. Yet their ambitions might be cruelly shattered by my appearance.

I inadvertently started this entry on the inside of the cover and front end paper of this, my third journal, which is already half-filled. I am usually so diligent about my record-keeping. I hope the spattering of blood and other marks across the page will be forgiven. At least the hand with which I write is mostly undamaged; I cannot say the same for my other.

Arnold Arboretum, Boston, 3 September, present day

Raising his glasses, Ben rested them on the savannah of his expansive forehead.

Either this required deep thought, or he needs reading glasses, mused Helen. Only the rustle of each page, slowly turned, stirred the silence as they sat side by side on the hard floor. Several increasingly awkward minutes passed before he spoke again.

'I'm almost lost for words, Helen,' he said softly, cradling the journal in front of him in both hands. 'This is something quite special you've discovered here.'

'There are more than one of those, too, and I think they're all written by the same person,' said Helen. 'Do you know who?'

He turned the journal over, tracing its tattered leather edges with his fingers, finally persuading his eyes to explore the collection of similar journals and papers in the box by his side. If there was a reply, it escaped him silently in a long exhalation. The professor seemed dazed.

Helen reached forward and removed, one by one, five more journals, some in good condition, others tattered like the first. Among them were several sheets of neatly folded cartridge paper tucked loosely in between some of the journals, and a larger volume of papers tied in a separate bundle below. 'These all seem to be letters, but from the quick look earlier, I think they're written by several different people,' she said, holding one out to him.

Ben looked at it, regarding it with obvious curiosity, but both his hands remained fixed on the book, as if it held all the answers to the mystery before them. 'You know,' he said finally, 'I think I might have an idea what these could be, and if I'm right, they could unlock a mystery that goes right back to the golden age of plant-hunting.'

Helen stood awkwardly, both legs now painfully numb from the hard floor. 'So… you didn't know these were here, and you think—'

'I can tell you, Helen, this has really got me thinking…' Ben paused while he struggled to stand, wincing in obvious discomfort. 'I'd like you to work on this, if you don't mind, as a special project for us. It would mean you'd have fewer opportunities to work across different disciplines in the arboretum, as I'd promised, but this could turn out to be a really big deal.'

Helen couldn't think of any reason to refuse such an offer, and this might mean she could visit other places as part of her research.

Ben had evidently already read her mind. 'Have you ever been to Scotland?' he asked.

Email: Arnold Arboretum, Boston, 4 September, present day

From: ben@arnoldarboretum.org

Dear Helen,

I was pleased to hear that you've got some bench space organised, and you're now on our email.

I am convinced that the author of the journals is John Jeffrey. I looked up a few articles about him in the library and came across this (below). Do make sure you meet with the librarian soon, as I know she will be only too pleased to show you how to search through our databases, catalogue etc. Also, Beatrix and Hanna (the two volunteers you met) really know their way around the stacks and archive, and are always keen to help.

This extract is from an 1872 article by Alexander Caulfield Anderson, who it seems knew Jeffrey personally – it may be the same Anderson in that first journal entry we read together (there's a coincidence!)? He makes it pretty clear that the plant hunter never made it back to Scotland. It only raises the question as to how we come to have his journals:

> *The late Mr Jeffrey, a botanist, who visited this country under the auspices of the Hudson's Bay Company, employed by the Duke of Buccleuch and other gentlemen to make collections, informed the writer that the grass in question appeared to be the most valuable for pasture of any he had ever met with. He collected a quantity of the seed, with a view to its propagation in Europe; but it is questionable whether it would thrive in any save the warm dry localities which are its natural habitat. It has the peculiarity that it never ceases to grow: thus, however apparently dry the exterior, the heart, shrouded from view, is always green, even in the depths of winter.*
>
> *Poor Jeffrey, it may be added, after wandering sometime in company with the writer through a considerable portion of British Columbia and braving all its fabulous dangers, met his fate in New Mexico in 1854. He was murdered by a Spanish outcast for his mules and his scanty travelling appointments.*

Source: Anderson, A. C. (1872). The Dominion at the West: A Brief Description of the Province of British Columbia, its Climate and Resources. The Government Prize Essay, 1872.

Fascinating stuff! Please keep me posted.
  Best,
  Ben

POLLINATION & FERTILISATION

1849–1850

THE INTRODUCTION OF GAMETES AND THEIR
UNION TO PRODUCE A SEED

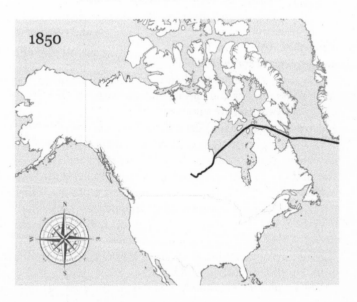

1850

Letter: Professor Balfour to HRH Prince Albert

Royal Botanic Garden Edinburgh
3rd August 1849

HRH Prince Albert
Buckingham Palace
London

Sir,

Oregon Botanical Association

I write on behalf of a proposed body, currently in formation, to be known as the Oregon Botanical Association.

Those involved in its establishment believe that it would be of great benefit to the interests of Arboriculture and Horticulture in our country to secure the introduction of new plant materials from the Western Parts of North America. Our intention is to secure the services of a Collector to follow in the footsteps of the late and celebrated plantsman, Mr David Douglas, who introduced so many novel trees and shrubs to our shores.

Our first requirement, following formalisation of the Association, will be to collect Funds sufficient to defray the necessary expenses of supporting the expedition. To this end we have secured, to date, formal expressions of interest from some eighty investors. These include many individuals known to you, including the Duke of Buccleuch, Earl of Burlington, the Lord Advocate, Lady Rolle and Lord Murray. Together with the organisation I represent, other notable botanical institutions will support the endeavour, including the Horticultural Society of London and the Royal Caledonian Horticultural Society. Certain well-regarded seed merchants, including Messrs James Veitch & Sons, are also enthusiastic Subscribers.

We would be honoured, Sir, if you were to consider

joining our list of Subscribers by lending your support in the form of an investment in the activities of the Association.

I have the honour to be,

Sir,

Your humble and obedient servant,

Professor John Balfour, Regius Keeper

P.S. I wish to mention how much I admire your efforts in the Society of Arts, and your energies in promoting the Great Exhibition planned at the Crystal Palace for 1851, by which time we intend that our Collector will be active amid the great trees of western North America.

Letter: Buckingham Palace to Professor Balfour

Buckingham Palace
London
21st August 1849

Professor Balfour, Regius Keeper and Her Majesty's Botanist Royal Botanic Garden Edinburgh

Sir,

I have received the Command of His Royal Highness Prince Albert to acknowledge receipt of your letter dated 3rd August, concerning the intended establishment of the Oregon Botanical Association.

His Royal Highness believes this to be a highly desirable endeavour that will diversify our country's best gardens and forests, improve their value and only expound our wonder in Nature. In particular, he believes that a personal investment may be prudent in support of his work in modernising the farms at Balmoral and Windsor.

I have been instructed to confirm that His Royal Highness wishes to purchase two shares. I would appreciate you sending the necessary paperwork to me at your earliest convenience.

Please do not fail to keep me abreast of developments so that I may keep His Royal Highness informed.

Your servant,

George Edward Anson, Private Secretary

HRH Prince Albert

Minutes: Oregon Botanical Association, Royal Botanic Garden Edinburgh, 22 November 1849 †

Minute of Meeting of Gentlemen interested in the promotion of the Arboriculture and Horticulture of Scotland.

Professor Balfour in the Chair.

On the Motion of Lord Murray, seconded by Mr George Patton it was unanimously resolved:—

- That it would be of great benefit to the interests of Arboriculture and Horticulture of Scotland to secure the introduction of the seeds of such of the Hardy Trees, Shrubs, and Flowers from the Western Parts of North America, as are suited to the climate of this country.

- That, considering the successful result of the labours of the late Mr Douglas in the collection of the seeds of useful trees and fine flowers and shrubs in that portion of the American Continent, the best method of attaining the benefits desired would be by securing the services of a Botanist of zeal and experience, who might be induced to follow in the steps of Mr Douglas, to complete his researches and to extend them in those parts of the country not fully explored by him.

- That a party particularly qualified for the undertaking may be induced to carry out these views, and that an effort should now be made for collecting Funds sufficient to defray the necessary expenses.

- That, with a view to raising the necessary Funds, each person willing to support the proposed shall subscribe the sum of L.5 or so many Sums of the like amount as they may please, each Subscriber being entitled for every such sum of L.5 to a corresponding Share of the Plants and Seeds which may be collected and from time to time sent home. No Subscriber to be liable for anything beyond the amount subscribed by him.

Letter: Andrew Murray to Professor Balfour †

15 Nelson Street,
Edinburgh
5th December 1849

To: Professor Balfour

Dear Sir,

Mr David Smith has handed me a copy of a Minute of the meeting of Arboriculturalists at which it was resolved to endeavour to collect funds to meet the expense of sending a Botanist to western America, to collect seeds and plants to be sent to this country and distributed among those who subscribed to the expense. As you were in the chair at this meeting and probably know more than anyone else as to the views and expectations of the originators of the scheme,

I think it better to trouble you with the suggestions I am going to make than anyone else.

Although I have a considerable interest in the improvement of our arboriculture, it is not so great as to induce me to subscribe £5 for the proposed expedition. But if you would add Entomology or even Coleopterology (to coin a word) to your botanical requisitions I would gladly subscribe a sum, and I have no doubt a considerable number of other men would be got to join.

You're probably aware that expeditions of this kind have been sent out by the entomologists of London to Colombia etc. I can imagine, however, that an obligation to collect insects in general would not only be thought, but be found to interfere materially with his botanical pursuits. This, however, would not be the case if you were to confine his collection of insects to Coleoptera. He could carry this out quite easily and simultaneously with his botanical researches.

I see from the Minute that you have some person in your eye whom you consider qualified. Perhaps it would do no harm to take his opinion as to the feasibility of the idea. To let him know more particularly what he would be required to do if he undertook to collect beetles, I enclose one of my circulars on the subject. After perusing, I should be glad to know whether you and he would be willing to admit Entomology into your plan, or if you think this would interfere with it.

I am, dear Sir,
Yours truly,
Andrew Murray

Letter: William Gibson-Craig to Professor Balfour †

H. M. Treasury
London
4th February 1850

Professor Balfour
Royal Botanic Garden
Edinburgh

My dear Sir,

I have been prevented from writing to you by a commission on the Public Offices which interferes much with my other business.

I was again at the Admiralty on Saturday and saw Sir F. Baring and Admiral Dundas about the grant of a passage to your Collector. As I expected, they consider that you must make a formal application to which an official answer will be given, before you publish anything regarding the assistance to be given by the Admiralty. They wish to know exactly what you want in case of any misconception or disappointment. You must therefore prepare a Petition, and if you get the Duke of Buccleuch to sign it as 'President of the Horticultural Society', while you sign as 'Professor of Botany' (with a few other signatures such as Lord Murray) it would give the scheme a sort of public character which might be useful. Enclose the Petition to me and I will take charge of it.

I am sorry to see you have as yet got so small a sum subscribed, and you really must make every exertion either to have the present subscriptions increased or to have them continued for two or three years. This should be done before you make new applications or put into circulation another list of subscriptions. As long as it shows generally only sums of £5 no one will think it is necessary to subscribe more, but if the example of more liberal donations is given it will probably in many cases be followed. If the Duke of Buccleuch, for instance, could be induced to give a sum of £50, with a few other subscribers of proportionate sums, it would at once give importance to the project, which would bring in many other contributions. I think it has been a great mistake starting it with all the subscriptions so low and I fear

you will have difficulty in getting sufficient funds, even at
the very low estimate you make for the expenses.
I am,
Yours very truly,
W. Gibson-Craig

Minutes: Oregon Botanical Association,
6 February 1850 †

Edinburgh

Present:
Professor Balfour
Lord Murray
Messrs George Patton, Isaac Anderson, Charles Lawson,
James McNab, David Smith, Andrew Murray

Professor Balfour in the Chair.

The Minutes of the last Meeting were read and approved.
Sir John McPherson-Grant now added to the Committee.
The advertisement proposed to be published was adjusted.
It is in the following terms:

'Botanical Expedition to Oregon.'

It appeared upon the attestation of Professor Balfour and
Mr McNab and the opinion of Dr Neill, stated by Lord
Murray, that Mr Jeffrey, presently employed in the Royal
Botanic Gardens, was a person eminently qualified for the
discharge of the arduous duties of Collector. It was thought
desirable that Mr McNab should communicate with Mr
Jeffrey stating that there was a probability of such an
appointment being planned. In his power, if the
Subscription Lists should be filled up, it was proposed that

at the expense of the Association he should receive lessons with reference to the mode of taking altitude and latitude & longitude. His attention was also to be called to the acquisition of a knowledge of the geography of the country. It was further resolved that his wages being 10/– per week should in the meantime be paid by the Association.

Minutes: Oregon Botanical Association's Sub-Committee, 20 February 1850 †

Edinburgh

Present:
Lord Murray
Lord Cunningham
Sir David Dundas
Professor Balfour
Messrs Andrew Murray, James McNab, David Smith, George Patton

Professor Balfour in the Chair.

The Meeting proceeded to consider the appointment of a Collector; Professor Balfour stated that various applications had been made for the situation, but from the very high recommendations that had been received of Mr Jeffrey the meeting thought he would be the fittest person. Before finally determining, however, they resolved first to see Mr Jeffrey, and appointed him to meet them at the Botanical Gardens on Saturday at three o'clock.

The Meeting requested Professor Balfour to ascertain what would be required in the way of instruments, which he undertook to do.

Letter: John Jeffrey to his parents

Edinburgh
Saturday, 23rd February 1850

Mr and Mrs J. Jeffrey
Lochleven Road
Lochore
Fife

My dear Sir and beloved Mother,

You both could never imagine the events that unfurled earlier today, even if you were to view my current situation with the greatest optimism. I was summoned this afternoon by Mr McNab, from the garden where I was employed on a menial task among the shrubbery, with an instruction to visit the rooms of Professor 'Woody' Balfour, our Regius Keeper. I had no choice but to attend in my work clothes, which I was rather ashamed about, on account of them being so untidy and my appearance overall so dishevelled. After all, no one would tackle a bank of dog roses in their Sunday best! I admit that I was fearful that some disciplinary matter was afoot, yet I was mistaken by some margin; as you will soon learn.

Naturally, I removed my hobnails under the archway of the offices before proceeding within. I admit that I was obliged to twist one sock a quarter to hide a hole that had become undarned! I knocked upon his heavy oak door with trepidation, as I could hear voices of more than one gentleman from within. 'Oh, Mr Jeffrey, welcome,' was how the Prof himself greeted me as he swung the door open, that bushy beard of his barely masking a broad grin. He then proceeded to apologise for taking me from my work, and for calling me without warning – imagine!

Prof Woody was at pains to make me feel quite at ease even though I felt short of stature, on account of my shoeless state, not to mention my unkempt appearance. He introduced me to four other gentleman, none of whom were known to me. One was Mr Andrew Murray, and I fear that I forget the name of the others. No matter, this Mr Murray – a most charismatic gentleman – introduced himself as the Secretary for a group of investors who call themselves the 'Oregon Association' on account of their interest in the plants found in that region of Western North America. It had come to their attention, he said, 'that I was a plucky man with energy and integrity'. You will only begin to imagine my awkward surprise, but he straight away explained that this opinion had been conveyed by Mr McNab, who had witnessed my tackling of a broken limb high up in a wind-damaged London plane in the garden. (I remember this well, as it was a particularly frightening event last spring, during which the tree was swaying violently in a storm which was yet abating!)

Anyway, forgive me, I am in danger of becoming distracted. I was invited to sit before these gentlemen and it was explained to me that they wished to conduct a formal interview for a position of some considerable privilege. 'You are familiar, we assume, with the impressive exploits of your fellow Scot, Mr David Douglas?' started Mr Murray. As you both know only too well – given my collection of books and pamphlets that I was so keen about in my youth – I was able to answer in the affirmative with considerable enthusiasm. This evidently pleased the gentlemen, who exchanged knowing smiles before Mr Murray continued, explaining that this Oregon Association had managed to secure funding sufficient to commission an expedition to North America. It was to follow in the footsteps of Mr Douglas – who so terribly lost his life there 16 years ago in that gory bull pit – and then adventure onwards.

One of the other gentleman – whose name I still cannot recall – asked me the scientific names of two botanical specimens he put before me, which I believe I answered well, while I expounded on some of their finer details. Curiously, he asked me rather vaguely what I knew of insects. I could only admit that, while I had a broad appreciation of their sorts, I was no specialist.

Even at this point in the conversation, I was unable to piece together the various facts apparently laid before me; it remaining quite unclear as to exactly what was being proposed. Only when the Prof, who until then had said little, added, 'My dear Mr Jeffrey, you seem befuddled! We are exploring whether you would consider becoming collector for the Oregon Association, and travelling to North America next summer?'

If I had not been sitting I may well have fainted from shock, such was the honour being bestowed upon me by these gentlemen. I'm sure that I barely managed to stammer an answer of sorts, but they evidently seemed pleased with my response and took turns to shake my hand. I am told that I am to return next week to learn more details about the planned expedition, and that I should think further about the nature of this endeavour, it being one that should not be agreed to lightly, given the distances and certain perils of travel in the Americas. Mr Murray explained that there would be no shame were I to reverse my decision after I had considered it at my convenience. Meanwhile, my wages will, from now on, be paid by the Association.

I apologise for going on so about my present circumstances, but I am extremely satisfied by this turn of events. I trust that you are both in rude health? I much appreciated your last parcel containing the fabulous cake, which I found most superior to Keiller's so-called 'Dundee'! I'll write soonest.

Your obedient and loving son,
John

Minutes: Oregon Botanical Association's
Sub-Committee, 23 February 1850 †

Edinburgh

Present:
Lord Murray
Professor Balfour
Messrs. Andrew Murray, James McNab, George Patton

Professor Balfour laid before the meeting the answers he had received to the Petition to the Admiralty (which were positive).

He also reported the result of his enquiries as to the instruments that would be necessary for the Collector.

Mr Jeffrey, the young man who was spoken of for that situation, was called in, and gave the meeting such information relative to his previous education and experience as they called for.

In consequence of the absence of Mr McIntosh and other members of the Sub-Committee, the meeting resolved to delay appointing the Collector till their sentiments should be ascertained on the subject.

Letter: Charles McIntosh to Professor Balfour †

Dalkeith Park
25th February 1850

To: Professor Balfour

My dear Sir,
I perfectly agree with you that very much of the success of the Oregon enterprise depends on the person who is sent

out, and in accordance with that impression I recollect how much I pressed for the offer of respectable remuneration. I think it was at one time proposed to give £60 or £70, though I thought £150 little enough; but did not state any objection at the last meeting when £100 was talked of. I was not at all aware until our first meeting in Queen Street that anyone had ever been thought of. I was standing my estimate upon the remuneration given by such men as Messrs Low, Veitch, Perry, the London Horticultural Society etc.

As soon as I found out that a party was named, and recommended by yourself, Dr Neill and Mr McNab, I offered no opposition, being perfectly well satisfied that neither of you would recommend a party unqualified for the task. Since then (and perfectly unacquainted with the young man Jeffrey) you will recollect I have been suggesting to the Committee the importance of giving him every opportunity of qualifying himself for so important a duty. I suggested nothing but that which I fairly considered to be the duty of the association towards the young man, and if acted upon, a few weeks would be sufficient to fit him for starting, at least in London where I think a week or two would be of importance to enable him to see the plants already brought home in a more developed state.

I thought all this was settled at the last meeting.

Your letter has taken me much by surprise, as I never had a doubt as to his qualifications.

One gentleman at the last meeting hinted to me something of the necessity of having a good man. In agreeing with him I said, 'As Professor Balfour, Dr Neill and Mr McNab have recommended a person, I do not like to start any objection.' Nor do I now, being well assured from my very intimate acquaintance with the late Mr Douglas, who when he first started knew little of either the geography or Botany of the country he went to, yet he did wonders. It is however to be borne in mind that Douglas went to an entirely new country and could hardly go wrong in picking up right and left. The case is now different. The Oregon and California have now been pretty well ransacked, and it seems to be most important that our Collector should know distinctly what is already in the country. Of this, no man limited to the Edinburgh collections can form a correct idea, but he may be greatly helped by spending a few weeks among the larger of all the collections in England. And in addition to this, I would think that he should be supplied with plain written descriptions of the trees and plants already sent home, and as regards the *Coniferae*, dried specimens of the principal species would help him much.

For myself, believe me when I say I will be perfectly content with whomever you send out, and for which this will be sufficient acknowledgement. With respect to others, I know that there are some who think otherwise, and in consequence have not subscribed. But in this case the Collector is of less consequence than the division of seeds.

I am very unwell but if I can, I will try to run in on Wednesday afternoon to the Botanical Garden, and if it is not intruding on your time may call on my way up to town. I am sadly vexed, as it seems predetermined that everything between us should be attended with unpleasant circumstances which I'm certain neither of us wish to cultivate.

I am yours very faithfully,
Chas. McIntosh

Minutes: Oregon Botanical Association's Sub-Committee, 28 February 1850 †

Present:
Lord Murray
Professor Balfour
Messrs. A. Murray, Macintosh, Patton, Smith

The Minute of the last Meeting was read and approved.

The salary of the Collector was then fixed at £80 a year but with the understanding that if the Committee be satisfied, the sum shall be increased to £100 the second year and £120 the third.

Mr John Jeffrey, presently employed in the Royal Botanic Gardens, was then appointed Collector for three years, but with power of the Committee at any time to terminate his engagement upon six months' notice.

The Secretary was directed to prepare the draft of an agreement between the Association and Mr Jeffrey to be submitted to next meeting of the Committee.

Professor Balfour undertook to prepare the draft of the instructions for collecting seeds to be furnished to the Collector before starting, and to write to Mr Darwin and other naturalists who had travelled on like expeditions for information on the subject.

Lord Murray was to write to Mr Rathbone in Liverpool and Mr Walker in relation to procuring a ship or free passage for the Collector if one of Her Majesty's Ships should be sailing at the time he is ready to start.

Provisional list of equipment:

- A dozen prismeters of small size. £3.3/– each.

- A small barometer – if the elevations are to be above 6,000 ft. £5 a good one, this Barometer would commence its indications at 5 or 6,000 ft. (£10.10/– filled up completely).

- Two thermometers for ascertaining temperature of boiling water. £2.2/– each. Regulating thermometers 35/–.

- Cooking apparatus, copper, £2.5/–.

- Compass 12/–.

- Case for compasses, tape measure, foot rule.

- Good watch.

- Pair of pistols.

- Sextant. 3 1/2 guineas.

- Map of Oregon 2/6.

- Map of America 5/6.

Letter: Charles Darwin to Professor Balfour

Down House
Farnborough
Kent
20th March 1850

Professor J. H. Balfour
Regius Keeper
Royal Botanic Garden
Edinburgh

My dear Professor Balfour,

I thank you for your letter concerning the excellent news about the imminent appointment of your Collector. You are to be congratulated on bringing your dream to life, and to have convinced so many impressive Subscribers to support your cause.

There is so much to say on the matter of the best preparations for your Collector that I believe it is more than I can impart in a simple letter. I wonder if you might wish to be our guest at Down, some time in the next month or two, when we could allow ourselves time to discuss the matter at some length?

I have also taken the liberty of writing to W. J. Hooker with your questions, who I know will have much to say. Perhaps, when your Collector is appointed, it could be arranged for them to meet together?

I hope that Mrs Balfour is quite well – pray remember me to her.

Yours sincerely,

C. Darwin

Email: Arnold Arboretum, Boston, 12 September, present day

From: helen@arnoldarboretum.org

Hi Ben,

Sorry for the delay in replying, but I wanted to make some progress before bothering you again. The lab is great, thanks, some fun company too.

I've been in touch with the librarian at the Royal Botanic Garden Edinburgh (RBGE) who's been really helpful. She's sent me a scanned version of the minute book of the Oregon Botanical Association (OBA), and the first few letters they've digitised.

I've been researching some of the backgrounds of those connected with it, either appearing in the minutes, in letters or among the list of subscribers. There are so many lords, sirs, earls, dukes, marquis, colonels, admirals... it's like reading the 1849 edition of *Who's Who* (funnily enough, that was the first year it was published!).

In addition to the obvious few – including Prince Albert and Charles Darwin! – many of them were very influential people. The chairman of the OBA was George Patton (Lord Glenalmond, judge and politician). Others included a Scottish baronet (Sir John MacPherson-Grant, whose family seat was Ballindalloch Castle), an admiral with the Royal Navy (Robert Mitford), a Scottish judge (Lord Murray), and several senior politicians such as Sir David Dundas (Solicitor General) and Sir William Gibson-Craig (Lord of the Treasury). There's also mention in one of the letters of

POLLINATION & FERTILISATION

Edward Ellice, who my research suggests can only be the politician and merchant nicknamed the 'Bear' thanks to his role in the fur trade (he was a director of the Hudson's Bay Company, HBC).

Looking at the subscribers, there were originally 143 shareholders. Among them, most had large country estates (e.g. William Murray of Henderland, Sir Robert Abercromby, the Duke of Devonshire, Duke of Buccleuch (also president of the Horticultural Society of London)), so they would have been keen to plant them with the new trees Jeffrey was sent after. Most had either one or two shares, while Prof Balfour must have stretched himself by purchasing three. Interestingly, the individual with the most shares (six) was William Gibson-Craig. Those with a commercial/professional interest in plants were also major shareholders, like Knight and Perry Exotic Nursery, and Veitch & Sons, plus the Horticultural Society of London (now the Royal Horticultural Society), and the Caledonian Horticultural Society.

Anyway, probably way too much information for you, but this is so interesting!

Thanks for the article. Like you say, if J J was murdered in New Mexico, I don't understand how we come to have his journals. Maybe he sent them off before his last trip, but you'd think they would have them in Scotland.

H.

Minutes: Oregon Botanical Association, 20 March 1850 †

Edinburgh

Present:
Prof Balfour
Sir John MacPherson-Grant

31

Sir David Dundas
Mr McNab
Mr D Smith
Mr Macintosh
Admiral Mitford also present.

Sir John MacPherson-Grant mentioned that he had had some conversation with Mr Edward Ellice as to the assistance which might be accorded to the Association by the Directors of the Hudson's Bay Company, were they applied to, and that Mr Ellice had given him reason to suppose that such assistance would be readily given.

The thanks of the Meeting were tendered to Sir John McPherson-Grant and Mr Ellice. The Secretary was directed to put himself in communication with Mr Ellice and if it was found that the Hudson's Bay Company would aid the Association by giving the Collector a passage across the country, it was resolved to avail themselves of their kinds.

The offer of Colonial Life Assurance to insure Jeffrey's life was laid before the Meeting and directed to be accepted.

Applications for letters of recommendation were directed to be made to the Foreign Office and American Ambassador.

The Secretary Mr Murray mentioned that in acknowledging receipt of the application by Dr Lindley for four shares in the Expedition on behalf of the London Horticultural Society, he has requested the perusal of the Journals kept by their Collector, and that Dr Lindley had kindly sent the Journal, which he then produced in the meeting. Mr Jeffrey the Collector is to see them with a view to making such notes that might be of use to the Expedition.

A. Murray

Letter: Edward Fillick to the
Oregon Botanical Association †

Balbirnie, Markinch
25th March 1850

D. Smith, Esq.,

Dear Sir,

I have only today received your letter of the 21st, forwarded to me from London. In consequence of a conversation with Sir George McPherson-Grant, I have already brought the matter you referred to under the consideration of the Hudson's Bay Company directors, and I am authorised to say that they will be happy to give every assistance in their power towards the object of your botanical expedition to the Oregon.

They will either give your Collector a passage in one of their regular ships sailing at the beginning of June to Hudson Bay, and thence in the Express canoe with the despatches, taking a route directly across the continent and through the northern passes up the Rocky Mountains; or should he determine to proceed by Panama and San Francisco to the Columbia, he will be furnished with a means of penetrating into the interior from the Company's principal stations at Fort Victoria on Vancouver Island, or at Fort Vancouver on the Columbia.

But as I shall be in Edinburgh tomorrow, it would be far better that I should see some of the individuals interested in the expedition, when I could explain matters more fully to them, and I shall be happy to do so if you would appoint any hour between ten and one o'clock on Wednesday for that purpose. I know it will find me if addressed to the new Club.

I remain, dear Sir,
Yours faithfully,
Edward Fillick

Detailed Instruction to the Collector,
Oregon Expedition †

Edinburgh
22nd May 1850

Sir,

1. You will on receipt proceed to London to join the Hudson's Bay Company's Ship *Prince of Wales* which leaves London for York Factory on the 8th June, and will sail for America on the vessel.

2. On your arrival at York Factory you will join the Brigade which proceeds to the West of the Rocky Mountains.

3. As the progress of this brigade is slow and subject to stoppages you will have opportunities of collecting en route, of which you will avail yourself.

4. The brigade will probably winter at Cumberland House, or at all events at some station to the East of the Rocky Mountains. You will remain with it, and as during the Winter you will be unable to prosecute the main objects of the Expedition, you will direct your attention to the collection and preservation of other branches of natural history, and to the acquisition of knowledge which may be useful to you in your subsequent travels. You will understand that the directions in this article apply equally to every Winter or space of time during which you may be unable to prosecute the main objects of the Expeditions.

5. In the following Spring you will again start with the brigade and continue with it (availing yourself of every opportunity of collecting) until you reach the Rocky Mountains.

6. On reaching these mountains it will be a matter for your consideration whether you remain behind, collecting in the Mountains, or proceed with the brigade to Fort Vancouver and return again with a party. This must depend very much upon circumstances, and the Committee leave it to your own discretion. It appears to them, however, that if on reaching the Rocky Mountains you either fall in with a party hunting or travelling in the Mountains, or can get such a party organised, it would be better that you remain with them and commence your researches at once.

7. Whether you so remain, or return after accompanying the brigade to its destination, you will, in exploring the Mountains, keep moving towards the northward if the state of the native tribes renders this practicable.

8. It will depend upon the success with which you meet how far you should proceed to the northward. Should you find that you are meeting with a rich harvest of the main objects of the Expeditions, you will extend your excursions as far to the northward as the season will permit, merely preserving sufficient time to reach a station suitable to winter at and convenient for starting to the northward again in the Spring of 1852.

9. Should you find that after proceeding to the northward your labour meets no adequate results, and should your enquiries with the natives and the hunters leave you no reason to suppose that a further advance to the northward will be more productive, you will turn towards the south and rest, and make for Vancouver Island.

10. Whether you reach Vancouver Island at the close of 1851, or starting for a more northerly station at the commencement of 1852 reach the Island during the Summer, you will decide sometime to its exploration. As is directed by the Committee that you will be able, not only to make a sufficient exploration of Vancouver Island during 1852, but also to make an excursion up the Columbia or in its neighbourhood.

11. If you are on the coast at the time the Winter sets in, either in 1851 or 1852, and you find that any of Her Majesty's vessels are sailing for the Sandwich other Islands in the Pacific, and that you can return to the Continent in time to prosecute your labours at the opening of the following Spring, at our will present the credentials from the Admiralty with which you will be furnished to the Captain of the Ship, and request to be favoured with a passage to these Islands, where you will spend the Winter reapplying your time in collecting for the Association.

12. On your return in the beginning of Spring and after having finished all you wish to do in Vancouver Island, you will proceed up the Columbia to the Rocky Mountains, and bend your course southward towards California. The Committee will, before that time, give you special instructions as to the point at which your Expedition will close. At present they do not contemplate extending it beyond San Francisco, from which port you will probably embark upon home, but it is possible that instead of extending your labours in California they may direct you to proceed through Mexico to return home by Vera Cruz or some port in the Gulf of Mexico. Special

instructions will be hereafter sent to you on this subject.

13. The foregoing instructions give you a general idea of the route that the Committee wish you to follow. They are aware that it must greatly depend upon circumstances which are beyond their cognisance and which can only be ascertained on the spot whether it would be judicious to adhere to these or not. Therefore, while they recommend you to follow them as far as may be practicable and judicious, they do not desire to fetter you to them. They leave you a large direction and power to follow that course which you may consider most likely to forward the objects of the Expedition. Whenever you see reason to deviate from your instructions, without having time to receive special instructions from the Committee, you will however communicate to the Committee your views and suggestions as to the most advisable route, that they may consider them, and direct you on your future course.

14. When you find the district in which you are engaged unproductive, you will not linger in it. When you fall on a rich and productive district, you will make it your headquarters for such period as may be necessary to enable you to examine it sufficiently – keeping in view that the great extent of ground over which it is intended the Expedition should be carried will not allow any unnecessary time to be wasted.

15. In exploring the Country for the objects of the Expedition, you will generally require to be accompanied by a party for protection and assistance. The numbers of which such a party must consist will vary at different times and in

different localities. You will receive every information and assistance on this, as well as upon every other point, from the officers of the Hudson's Bay Company, who will also aid you in procuring proper assistance. The Committee particularly direct that you shall on no account take an insufficient escort from any design. To diminish your expenses, they suggest that you may find means considerably to save the funds of the Association by joining hunting parties who are going in the same direction as you, or by getting them for a consideration to direct their Expedition by the route you wish to follow.

16. So long as you continue in the territories of the Hudson's Bay Company, you will need no money. Whatever articles you require will be furnished to you by the Company. For these supplies you will grant receipts, which will be transmitted to the Committee by the Hudson's Bay Company.

17. When you leave their territories, you will in the same way be supplied by the Company with what funds you require either at Fort Vancouver on the Columbia, or at Fort Victoria, Vancouver Island.

18. The foregoing instructions apply more particularly to the route to be followed by you. The Committee now beg your attention to the duties to be performed by you during the expedition. You will write to them at every opportunity, giving them a full account of your progress. You will address your letters and packages to the Professor of Botany in the University of Edinburgh.

19. You will also keep a daily journal in which you will note down your proceedings, and the

observations mentioned, along with anything you may observe interesting or curious, particularly with regard to the plants or objects of natural history which you may collect. You will keep a duplicate copy of this Journal in case of one being lost. You will write the Journal in the small books furnished by the Committee, and as each small book is finished you will despatch one copy to the Committee at the first opportunity. You will keep the duplicate copy until you have heard of the safe arrival of the other, when it also may be sent.

20. You will keep a daily register of the temperature of the places where you are, and also record your observations as to their climate, its dryness or moisture.

21. When you remain stationary for some days at any place, you will endeavour to ascertain and record the mean temperature of the place by finding the temperature of the ground three feet below its surface.

22. You will also ascertain the altitude of the various places where you gather seeds.

23. You will collect seeds of all such trees, shrubs and plants as are not already introduced into this Country, more particularly those which are likely to thrive in the open air in this Country, and in a special manner you will devote your attention to the collection of the seeds of Coniferae, both those already introduced into the Country, and those which may be new to it – and also of the hardy trees likely to be valuable in plantations. The quantity of each seed which you will collect must be considerable, if possible at least as much as will supply two hundred persons with a few seeds each. Some of the seeds should be gathered

and transmitted in their cones and seed pods so as to indicate the nature of the plants.

24. After the seeds are gathered you will spare no pains to keep them in a dry state. You will pack them carefully and transmit them to Britain in the most approved manner, as to which you will receive separate instructions from Professor Balfour and Mr McNab.

25. On the outside of each package of seed you will put a mark or number corresponding to a similar one in your Journal, where you give such information as to the plant, its nature and locality, and the soil, temperature and altitude of the place of its growth as you may be able to furnish. In the case of trees, you will note their height, diameter and nature of the wood. Besides this you will make a Memorandum on the outside of the package, giving concisely the most essential part of this information in case of the Journal being lost.

26. Whenever an opportunity occurs you will transmit such seeds and other articles as you may have collected, and you will always endeavour to get the packages sent across the Continent by the Hudson's Bay Company's men. When you are on the Western Coast and cannot get this done, you will send your packages to the Country via Panama, making use of your credentials to the officers of H. M. Ships to get them conveyed free of charge. You will not, unless you have a superfluity of seeds which cannot easily by conveyed otherwise, send any seeds round by Cape Horn or the Cape of Good Hope. You may send dried specimens or heavy articles, or seeds packed in alternate layers of earth by that route.

27. You will whenever practicable preserve five dried

specimens of the plants whose seeds you collect, and affix the same mark to them as is placed on the package of seeds and in the Journal. You will also endeavour to send five dried specimens of all the plants you may meet with in the regions you visit, unless you know that the plant is already introduced into this Country. Your attention is also to be directed to Cryptogamic plants.

28. You will collect every beetle you can find in the course of your travels, searching for them at the same time as for plants and seeds. In the winter you will examine carefully under the bark of trees and generally follow out the directions for collecting and packaging them given by Mr Murray in his printed directions, of which you are furnished with copies.

29. You will dry the small beetles and keep them among cotton in the tin boxes. The larger ones will be sent in the bottles. You will put those which have been taken in any district in a different box or bottle for those taken in another, marking the region from which they have been taken. The extent of the region which you may include in one bottle is considerable – all those taken within two or three hundred miles of the East coast of America may be included in one region. Those taken in the Central part of America should form another. Those taken on the Rocky Mountains form another, and perhaps those taken on the East flank and West flank should be separated, and those taken on the Western side of these Mountains should form another. Those taken in the different degrees of latitude must also be separated, but it may be sufficient to make a separation at every fifth degree of latitude.

30. You will also collect sea and land shells as you meet with them. You will often find them when looking for beetles, and when small you may put them into the phial among the beetles.

31. You will, when you can do so without interfering with the main objects of the Expedition, collect such objects of natural history or general interest as have been already alluded to in Article four, but you will never forget that everything is subordinate to the collecting of seeds and beetles, particularly the former.

32. You will find it of material advantage to endeavour to incite a taste for the objects of your pursuits, or in other branches of natural history, among the men composing the party with whom you may be travelling. You will also find the Indians most useful assistants in procuring specimens of what you require, it having been found in almost every country which collectors have traversed that a large proportion of the most valuable specimens have been got by employing the natives. You are therefore strongly recommended to avail yourself of such assistance, which you will obtain for a mere trifle.

These are the general instructions which the Committee have now to give. Further and more special instructions will be sent out to you as circumstances may require.

Minute of Agreement between the association for procuring seeds from Oregon and John Jeffrey, 24 May 1850 †

It is Contracted, Agreed Upon and Ended between the parties following *viz*. John Hutton Balfour M.D., Professor of Botany in the University of Edinburgh, Chairman, and David Smith, Writer to the Signatory, Treasurer of the Association organised for sending out a Collector to the western parts of America, to procure and send home seeds and plants, and certain objects of Natural History to this country, and as authorised by the Committee appointed for the management of the same to subscribe to this deed on their behalf, as per Minute of Meeting, dated the twenty-fourth day of May, Eighteen hundred and fifty, on the one part, and John Jeffrey, now or lately employed in the Royal Botanic Garden Edinburgh, on the other part, in the manner following. That is to say, the said John Hutton Balfour, and David Smith, hereby agree with and hire the said John Jeffrey to make a voyage to America, and to traverse such a part thereof or of the neighbouring islands and nearest countries, as may be directed to do so by the Committee.

This said, John Jeffrey shall be bound from time to time to transmit or furnish the said John Hutton Balfour, in terms of his instructions, with his Journal, while engaged under the Association, and of which the committee of the Association shall be entitled to make any use they may think proper.

This said, the Association hereby agrees with the said John Jeffrey that he shall be entitled out of the funds to receive the sum of Eighty Pounds as wages or salary for the period during which he shall continue in the employment of the said Association. The sum shall be increased to one hundred pounds for the second year, and one hundred and twenty pounds for the third. That said, the Association also agrees that the said John Jeffrey shall receive out of the said

Fund all reasonable expenses including his own board and travelling charges that he may make in the prosecution of said journeys.

Signed

John Jeffrey | J. H. Balfour | David Smith

Witnesses

J. Law Black | William B. Reid

Email: Arnold Arboretum, Boston, 3 October, present day

From: helen@arnoldarboretum.org

Hi Ben,

I feel I'm making some decent progress now. It's hard to believe that I've been here one month today!

The RBGE librarian has sent across more OBA letters, along with Jeffrey's contract, which makes interesting reading. In this, Jeffrey is asked to keep journals in duplicate, sending both to Edinburgh in separate consignments.

The writing is quite difficult to decipher in some of the letters – occasionally it has taken about an hour to understand just a few lines, and I've sometimes needed another pair of eyes to decipher a specific word! Generally, though, I think I'm getting more proficient.

I've realised that J J was the same age as my older brother when he left on the expedition (just over 23 yrs) – I can't imagine him following in J J's footsteps at such an age!

I've not yet heard back from the Regius Keeper about a possible visit, but I'll keep you up to speed.

Best,

Helen

Journal: London, England, 1 June 1850

The Great Oregon Expedition is underway, and I am its explorer! With these words I commit to my journal for the first time, and they fill me with pride and excitement, if not a little trepidation.

Prof Woody and the other gentlemen did not demand that I write a journal until I arrive in the Americas, yet I find myself keen, being already inspired by the journey before me. I made up my mind to record some notes so I may become at ease writing in my own company.

I arrived in London four days ago. On Wednesday, I met Mr William Gibson-Craig at Her Majesty's Treasury (after two unsuccessful attempts). He was ill-prepared for my arrival, thinking I was coming another day, but of more concern, once we got to discussing the expedition, was his evident disappointment with the financial arrangements made for me by the Association. He told me he will write with some urgency to attend to this, hoping that new information may reach me even while I am still this side of the Atlantic.

Mr Craig took me to East India House on Leadenhall Street, which was a most imposing building from the outside, but so dim within that candles burned even during the day. I met many very knowledgeable gentlemen who, in a short time, passed on to me a great deal of practical information to help with my planned work and travel.

During the intervening days I visited Dr Lindley at the University, and also met Sir William Hooker at Kew Gardens. The former was positive and extremely helpful in all manner of practical aspects, while the latter was quite the foreboder. Sir William seemed dissatisfied overall with the planned operations as they stand, and, I think it true to say, the very intentions of the Association itself.

I have required further materials for the expedition. In total, I've expended £49.10s.2d., with major articles of clothing now among my baggage, including breeches, stockings and boots. I also secured a new sort of hat, called a bowler; I thought it expensive (10s.), but being designed with gamekeepers in mind I believe it will be a hardy companion. In addition, I now have two thick coats that I'm confident will keep the worst of any winter cold at bay. I was allowed £20 for the purchase of instruments and books.

I have purchased six robust leather-bound journals – like this one – for the record that I am contracted to keep. I still have those provided by the Association, but I thought them too small; they may yet serve as an alternative for notes of a different sort. I cannot imagine I will be able to write enough to fill all these journal pages, nor that I will have so much to mention.

John Jeffrey,
Explorer, Oregon Botanical Association

Letter: William Gibson-Craig to Andrew Murray †

H. M. Treasury
London
3rd June 1850

Mr Andrew Murray

My dear Sir,
By most extraordinary oversight you were allowing Jeffrey to set off without having made any arrangements as to how he is to be supplied with Funds, or to what amount he is to be allowed to draw. Neither he nor Mr Ellice have any instructions on the subject, and the latter has come to me to know to what amount Jeffrey is to have a Credit on the Hudson's Bay Company, and on whom his drafts are to be made, stating at the same time that as a business transaction the Company must have a letter to

that effect in order that the Credits may be entered in their books and directions sent out to their Agents. The vessel sails tomorrow and I do not know what to do. You have sent me no information as to the intentions of the Committee, who appeared to have overlooked altogether this most important arrangement considering the inaccessible country into which Jeffrey is to be despatched.

I shall see Mr Ellice tonight and make the best arrangements I can with him, as there is no time to lose and Jeffrey must be secured in Funds, but you must instantly send up a letter, enclosed either to me or Mr Ellice, establishing a Credit for him with the Company to such amount as you think proper, and stating on whom Jeffrey is to draw. The communication being so difficult and uncertain, I think the Credit should provide for his expenses for at least two years, and you can specify if you choose that only a certain sum is to be advanced in each year. While with the Company he must not require actual cash, but all necessaries or articles for which payment to the natives is required will be charged to him at their prices by the Agents, and he must give a bill for them as if he had received money. Send this letter of Credit if possible by return of Post, because Jeffrey tells me the vessel remains some days at Stromness, and it is possible that letters from London may catch it there before its departure.

Jeffrey ought to have been here 10 days sooner than this and many other arrangements might have been made. I never saw him till Wednesday when I was obliged to be all day in a Committee, but I took him yesterday to the East India House, and got for him from Dr Boyle and Dr Downing all the information they could give him as to racking, preserving and sending home seeds etc. I have also got him from Lord Palmerston and the Admiralty official letters to all Consuls of the West Coast of America and Mexico, and commanders of H. M. Ships in the Pacific, directing them to give him every assistance, but more might have been done had there been more time.

In great haste,
Yours very truly,
W. Gibson-Craig

P.S. Jeffrey himself has not the slightest idea what funds are to be at his disposal, or what expense he may properly incur. This is entirely omitted in his instructions, and the Committee should give him generally their views upon the subject. I shall let you know tomorrow what I arrange with Mr Ellice.

Journal: Gravesend, England, 8 June 1850

I arrived here via the first coach of the morning, after a journey of 23 miles from the City of London. I had no trouble in finding a seat in one of the many stages that plies this route. I admit that London was almost too much for my senses. I couldn't fully comprehend its enormity, and the great number of people living there. It made Edinburgh seem very much a provincial town in comparison, despite its elegance.

I had expected to sail this afternoon, but even before I set off to the docks themselves I was informed, by more than one friendly soul, that the ship's departure had been delayed for some days. I cannot pretend that I'm not disappointed, but a short rest will allow me to recover from the bustle of London.

I have found an inn to lodge in at Gravesend Reach, from where I write now. It is a busy place, thronging with rowdy seamen, with much mafficking in the streets. The town itself is crowded with buildings, many of which seem to be inns and taverns. The whole place appears to be tumbling down from its mound into the Thames itself.

On depositing my luggage, I resolved to visit the waterfront, and there I was rewarded with a rare sight. I estimate on the water there were no fewer than 200 vessels of all types, moving in every direction, the fishing craft crossing with the ferries, tilt boats and busy pilots. Before the tide turned, they gathered in ever greater numbers, waiting to continue their journey upstream towards London. In the distance, I could just make out a vast stationary object I believed to be one of the infamous prison hulks. It was too far distant to observe whether those moving about on the decks had the Devil's claws about their person.

I eventually reached the East India Dock to meet my transport to the Americas. There were a great number of people and activities on its banks, the smells and sights assaulting my senses. Quite the worst sort was a cargo of guano being unloaded by some wretched souls to whom the stench seemed to matter little. Evidently, this material is transported around the globe as a commodity, this particular cargo hailing from the Americas.

My ship is the *Prince of Wales*. She is a fine-looking craft. I conversed with one of her sailors on the dockside, who spoke about her with some affection, naming her type a barque. He pointed out her defining features – three main masts and a square stern – and it was his opinion that she is almost as fast as the largest ships of our time, but run by a smaller and more expert crew. Not without a little mischief, he informed me that this is the second HBC ship of that name, the first having been lost to a floating iceberg in 1821. I am told she is 500 tons, and her sleek looks give me some cheer for the crossing. My informant seemed to know little about our delay, merely shrugging as if it were no matter to him or anyone else.

Letter: William Gibson-Craig to Professor Balfour †

H. M. Treasury
London
8th June 1850

Professor Balfour
Royal Botanic Garden
Edinburgh

My dear Sir,

On meeting Mr Ellice last night he told me that Mr Murray of Henderland had authorised him to enter a Credit for Jeffrey to the amount of £200, which was just what I intended to have done. I have seen Mr Murray this morning who is in the same amazement as myself at the conduct of the Committee. To start a man on such an expedition into the remotest and most inaccessible parts of the world without making any arrangement whatever as to how he was to be supplied with money, is the most extraordinary proceeding I have ever heard of. Besides, Jeffrey ought to have been here at least a fortnight or three weeks sooner. There is an immense amount of most valuable information (almost indispensable to his success) upon everything connected with his mission which I could have put him in the way of obtaining, but there was no time to do anything, and never having been out of Scotland before, the lad was quite bewildered by the number of things he had to attend to.

Mr Ellice tells me he thinks there is no probability of letters overtaking the vessel at Stromness, but another ship will be despatched in September with the later despatches, which he believes will reach Jeffrey at his winter quarters. Mr Ellice leaves London about the 17th inst., and as it is most desirable to arrange with him the credits for Jeffrey while he's here, you must get the committee to settle immediately the financial scheme. You must bear in mind the very great uncertainty of Jeffrey receiving letters as soon as he crosses the Rocky Mountains, and as he may be obliged to find it expedient to alter his route or expedite his journey, he should also be informed now where he will find credits after leaving the territory of the Hudson's Bay Company. Let me know the earliest day you can what the committee determines, and I will consult with Mr Ellice as to how their views can be best carried out, but if this is not most carefully arranged Jeffrey must be placed in the greatest difficulties and the scheme will fail. It is incomprehensible to me how you should have entirely overlooked this, the most essential part of the whole arrangements.

I am,

Yours very truly,

W. Gibson-Craig

Letter: John Jeffrey to Professor Balfour †

Ship *Prince of Wales*
Gravesend
11th June 1850

To Professor Balfour

Sir,

I must confess I have been far out of my duty for not writing you some days since, to make known to you the way I was treated in London. I hope you will be pleased to forgive me – time passed as long as I was in London almost unknown to me. I left on Saturday morning with the expectation of sailing that afternoon, but owing to some mismanagement they have been detained till this time, Tuesday morning. We expect to be off in the course of an hour. I have been exceedingly fortunate in getting a fine ship – I think I shall be as comfortable as I could wish. The Captain appears to be a particularly good man. There are in all 10 of us in the cabin, some going out to remain as Factors to the Company.

I am happy to be able to inform you that I met with the greatest degree of kindness from all parties that I called upon round London. I am much indebted to the great interest Dr Lindley took in me – he took great trouble instructing me on all points that he thought would be advantageous to my success. After he had given me all the information that he thought I could absorb, he gave me a note for Mr Munro, desiring him to show me anything that I wished, so I spent the day with Mr Munro. He took great trouble showing me all the plants from North America. I went over Douglas's and Hartweg's collection of specimens. Mr Munro pointed out what had been lost since being introduced by them, and what had never been introduced. I hope to profit from the information which I gained at this establishment through the liberality of Dr Lindley.

I went on the following day to Kew. I saw Sir William Hooker. He was kind enough, but I could see something about him that he did not think he had been perhaps consulted enough about it. From what he said, he alluded to the very quiet way the expedition had been kept and, what was worse than all, he was very disheartening as to the likelihood of my success. He told me they had a Collector out, just on the same route that I am taking, for four years, and he did no good at all. I earnestly hope that such will not be the case with me. I told him that there was no reason why another might not be successful, for it is well known there are things there, although not new, that would pay for the trouble. Then he spoke of there being some years that there is not a cone to be found in all the country. To confirm his statement, he brought to my notice that some years there is no Beech mast in this country. I hope I will be fortunate enough to match his year of plenty.

I may mention but I have seen no pines that I did not see in Scotland of some sorts – they had better specimens, such as those at Dropmore Garden.

I must not neglect the kindness I received from Sir W. Gibson-Craig. I went to the Treasury on the Monday after I came to town but I was unfortunate enough not to find him, so I called back again on the Tuesday and was equally unfortunate, but I left my letter of introduction and my address. So I had a note next morning wishing me to call upon him at his house, which I did, and I must say I found him all that I could desire. He went about forwarding my arrangements with great heart. He got me a letter from the Admiralty and likewise one from Lord Palmerston for all the British Consuls that lie on my route. He likewise accompanied me to the Indian House to see what information he could pick up as to the most successful mode they adopted for packing their seeds. The gentleman that I came in contact with in this establishment was Dr Royle – a kind gentleman and very willing to assist me. His extensive practice had made him best acquainted with the best packing system used to preserve items on the journey to and from India.

There was one thing that seemed to put Sir W. Gibson-Craig about a little, and this was his not receiving right information concerning my money and affairs, this being an omission I suspect, some way or other, the exact sum not being mentioned, but I expect that will be made right and my letters of credit will await me at Stromness, at which place we expect to reach perhaps about the 20th June.

I mentioned when I wrote to Mr McNab to forward the stamp there. I am all in order for my harvest, if it will be the will of God to continue to Bless me with the same bountiful supply of health which he has been graciously pleased to bestow on me in time past. I am in excellent spirits, fearing nothing that may be before me. I still think that I will in some measure be able to make some returns that will recompense all connected with the mission. I am supposing the Kew Collector who got nothing might perhaps have been at the diggings or somewhere else, where his own interest was more in view than those of his employers.

I have made up my mind the better I serve you, I will at the end find I have been serving myself, so at all events if I should not be successful, I shall not have to reflect on not having done my duty.

I will write from Orkney to Mr McNab, God willing. I wrote him just on the morning that I received his letter.

I am, Sir,

Your Humble Servant,

John Jeffrey

Journal: Afloat, 11 June 1850

The less I mention of the last few wasted days the better. Suffice to say that I have seen all that Gravesend has to offer. Now at last we are all on board, and for the first time I write while afloat.

Last evening, I was invited along with the captain – Mr David J. Herd – and the ship's surgeon to attend a farewell banquet onshore, which is customary on the last evening before departure of the HBC ship. I have never eaten so much fine food and tasted wine as we did. Afterwards, on returning to the ship, finding my berth in the dark was no easy matter, made worse by the effects of the evening's excesses.

Early this morning, I wrote to Prof Balfour to inform him of my activities and preparations while in London, making sure the letter was on its way before we set sail.

We were towed from our mooring at the East India Dock by oarsmen in two small boats, on account of the wind being unfavourable. A great deal of signal firing accompanied our departure, as did a few tearful relatives who waved farewell to some of my new companions until they were too distant to see clearly.

I am lucky to have a fellow cabin-mate who is a most companionable sort. The two of us have plenty of room to live comfortably and find solace there when elsewhere it is bustling. He's a young man going to Red River in Rupert's Land, where he has an appointment as a teacher. He tells me he will be living in Fort Garry, which is the centre for those working in the fur trade in this area, and a major trading post for the HBC. On looking together at the map of North America supplied to me, we believe this to be further south than my likely route, which will take me through the Saskatchewan District.

This evening we dined with the captain, who appears to be a most interesting gentleman and a very experienced sailor. I learned we are to journey some eight days to Stromness in the Orkney Isles, following a course to North America which the sailors call 'north-about'. The main reason for the north-about is to take advantage of easterly winds across the Atlantic Ocean, starting from our point of departure at the tip of Great Britain. To reach there, first we will start by the North Sea, as this is more favourable than the alternative of travelling the English Channel and then northwards along Britain's west coast; we thereby avoid the vicious currents and innumerable obstacles in those parts.

We are to select some new crew at Stromness, and collect additional passengers who more than likely will work for the Hudson's Bay Company (HBC) in the Americas. We will also take on water and provisions in readiness for the main crossing.

Tonight, the sea is calm and I find writing no ordeal. Some of my companions, however, already seem a little green.

Journal: North Sea, 20 June 1850

We have been at sea for eight days. At times it has been quite an adventure on account of some stormy weather during recent days. Captain Herd tells us we will reach Stromness tomorrow morning, after rounding Pentland Firth some time this evening. I learned for the first time that we may be some weeks at the Orkneys, taking on provisions and new passengers, and perhaps making other arrangements I cannot imagine.

We have traversed the entire length of the eastern seaboard of England, keeping close to her shore, so land was often in sight. I was raised from my berth by a commotion on deck when Flambro' Head was sighted. Its arches and deep sea caves were magnificent. The next day we passed the piles of Tynemouth Castle, this being my last glimpse of England. The weather changed later that day and it's been the last land we've had sight of.

While the weather was still fine, we were lucky to witness a great shoal of mackerel surfing our bow wave. Their flanks shone brilliantly, and there were so many they made a curious rushing sound as they broke the surface.

There has been little else to entertain me on this leg of the journey. Now I understand we are to pause so long at another port, I feel that I've yet to embark on the main adventure. I begin to realise that long-distance travel requires a great deal of patience, being as I am, entirely in the hands of others.

Journal: Stromness, Orkney, 21 June 1850

Our arrival at Stromness, early this morning, attracted a great deal of attention among the islanders. The north-west ship, as they apparently call it, is evidently an important feature in the Orcadians' year.

Our approach was greeted by all on board with great cheer, with the deck filling with passengers even before the sun rose. The Orkney Islands are rugged, small and greatly exposed. In many places, magnificent sea cliffs rise hundreds of feet sheer from the sea, with even higher mountains behind, and elsewhere I glimpsed deep bays with startling white sand.

The sheltered harbour where Stromness nestles is full of many hundreds of vessels, almost as busy as the River Thames, although here they are mostly fishing boats. The north-west ship has its own designated berth, and a great throng of locals were about as we docked.

The town itself hugs the bay, the houses gripping tenuously to the hillside, their crow-stepped gables painted in white and sometimes gay colours. Even some of their walls meet the sea itself. They were a pretty sight from the ship.

Once ashore, I walked the stone-flagged main street which is crowded with houses and shops. It follows the contours of the hill like a wayward deck rope, sometimes rising and falling with steps. I cannot imagine how carts can travel along it. I think it less attractive close-up than from afar, not least because of the pervading smell of fish, but its shops and taverns seem well suited to our needs. I'm confident I'll be able to purchase provisions of winter clothing that some on board have advised me to look for in various stores.

I passed Logan's Well, from where water will be collected for the ship. Talking about it in a tavern this evening, a local man proudly told me it was the same well from which Captain Cook drew water for his ships *Resolution* and *Discovery*. I realised that this place must also have been the last known landfall of Sir John Franklin's expedition, which sailed five years ago to chart the Northwest Passage. His two ships, and all their men, have still not been found. Only this year, more British ships have gone again in search of those poor frozen souls, no doubt also eager to claim the £20,000 reward offered by the Admiralty. If I were to disappear, I doubt whether there would be any search party sent after me, although I suppose that the subscribers may be disappointed by the failure of their investment.

Journal: Seabirds, 22 June 1850

I returned to town yesterday afternoon and secured my final provisions, especially some very fine winter undergarments. All folk were very welcoming and eager to hear about my reasons for travelling. I think many found the idea of the expedition a little frivolous, but perhaps among people whose only experience of trees is of the dwarf and twisted sort, they cannot imagine the value of this mission.

Today, I went to the cliffs with my gun, in the company of an officer from the ship and a local boy who brought with him a long-handled net. The cliff crests are carpeted everywhere with thrift, mingling together with pink campion and sea squill, which lend them an alluring pinky hue, though these spring flowers are now mostly spent. There we shot and netted many birds and were quite spoiled for choice. We secured petrel, puffin, kittiwake and gannet, and I practised – with some help from my local companion – the art of skinning them. I thought this an essential skill for my expedition so that I might preserve the skins of some of the birds of America. The rainbow beaks of puffins are even more beautiful when seen close at hand, especially at this time during their breeding.

We brought back the puffin breasts for our evening meal; we had more than enough for the officers and passengers. They tasted very fine.

Journal: Sunday, 26 June 1850

With the captain and most of the ship's company we travelled to Sandwick, about 4 miles north of Stromness, to attend Holy Communion. The kirk was only a small building, yet I counted more than 400 in the congregation, even before our own numbers swelled theirs. Its creamy harled walls are only a pebble's throw from the sea. The hearty singing, friendly congregation and overall exposure of the place left a great impression with me.

Afterwards, we were invited to lunch at the manse by Rev Charles Clouston. It seems that the reverend is a great observer of all natural wonders. I noticed he kept all manner of instruments at one of his large upstairs windows, overlooking the sea. He records the diversity and numbers of seabirds, and was justly proud of a vast collection of their eggs which he had arranged in the drawers of a chest in his study. It is strange that the eggs of the puffin, surely the showiest bird in all of Britain, are the plainest.

He also keeps a detailed botanical diary, and he was keen to teach me everything he could about the plants of Orkney during the short time we had together. I learned much about some new species from his pressed collections, including the uncommon *Primula Scotica* (the dainty full-sized specimen measured less than 2 inches in height), which sadly was in flower before my arrival, and will likely be again after I have departed. He had made a good impression of the tiny plant in a watercolour, showing its deep pink petals and yellow eye.

The reverend told us a curious story about patterns of sunlight he sometimes observes over the sea. He described these as a perpendicular column of light that can appear shortly before sunrise or sunset, and which can last for several minutes. He was at a loss to explain this phenomenon, but we encouraged him to contact some person from the Royal Society who may 'shed some light' on the matter.

Journal: Skaill, 26 June 1850

I went with the captain and a couple of fellow passengers to the Manor House at Skaill. In the afternoon and before dinner, our host, Dr William Watt, showed us a most beautiful bay, whose pale sands were protected from the sea and wind, which seem always so violent here. From a vantage point, we could see waves breaking through a great cave which passes completely through a headland. It is known as Hole O'Row.

Some local ladies came with us for the excursion. They were most keen on the botany of the sea plants or Algae, and tried to enthuse me about their properties and to help with their taxonomy. I fear I was less taken by the botany than I was by the company of the fairer sex. The most interesting thing that I was able to learn was about which of the Algae the Orcadians regularly include in their diet. However, I also learned that the women of this place are quite lonely while so many of the menfolk embark on great voyages to the Americas.

At sunset, a couple of us stood atop a large, curious and irregular grass-covered mound that the locals call Skerrabra. Our host held to a theory that it is unnatural, and that it harbours some hidden ancient treasure. The wildness of that place left quite an impression. As we gazed together across the vastness of the Atlantic, I imagined the molten orb touching the land on which I may soon be standing, God willing.

Journal: Hill of Hoy, 27 June 1850

I travelled alone today, wanting to explore Hoy. It was a short smooth sea crossing, skirting round tiny Graemsay Island, to reach the island of Hoy. I walked 5 miles to ascend the main hill that has been dominating the view for all the time that I've been here. The Hill of Hoy stands proud of others near about.

The weather was very clear, and even the wind unusually calm. I was rewarded with spectacular views north, across the sea to the main island. The town of Stromness seemed so far below, I felt I was one of the thousands of soaring seabirds. I could even make out the Pierhead and the *Prince of Wales*; it reminded me of a toy ship I was once so fond of as a child.

I used the occasion to practise the measurement of altitude with my barometer, it being convenient that I had started my walk at sea level. I estimated the hill's peak to be 1,558 feet. It was high enough to support many of the same alpine plants that I've observed on hills of greater altitude on the Scottish mainland, including purple saxifrage (*Saxifraga oppositifolia*) which is very hardy. The reverend had mentioned that this plant was edible; this I found to be true, the initial bitter taste of its flowers quickly turning to a delightful sweetness.

The vantage point confirmed the treeless nature of the Orkneys, with no woods to be seen in any quarter of the compass. Only the occasional twisted soul of a birch or rowan, clinging to life among the boulders, suggests that any forests may once have existed here.

I descended via the north slope which proved an exciting scramble, especially in twilight. I only just made the last boat back to Stromness. I'm unusually tired this evening.

Journal: Ready to depart, 29 June 1850

The ship is ready and apparently all preparations made ready for the crossing. We have taken on mutton, fresh beef and eggs, and also some livestock of some half-dozen pigs, numerous ducks and hens, and several geese. Many Orcadians have joined us, too; some to serve on the ship, others with the HBC when we reach the Americas. They all seem a hardy sort.

Like the ship, I am ready too. I have seen all this place can offer, and now I'm anxious to get underway.

The navigator, Mr Starr (yes, truly!), says we must wait for a favourable wind, but at present, there is a strong westerly that makes it impossible to leave the harbour.

I've started a letter to Professor Balfour which I'll send before we depart.

Letter: John Jeffrey to Professor Balfour †

Ship *Prince of Wales*
Stromness
Orkney Islands
July 1st 1850

To Professor Balfour

Sir,

You must all be longing to hear from me that you may be able to know how I have spent my time since I left London, as I mentioned to you in my last that we left Gravesend on the 11th June. After a boisterous crossing of nine days we made this place. I find that sea-sickness does not appear to take hold of me from the number of the passengers all being sick, and I quite flatter myself that I am to make a good sailor.

Since our arrival here I have spent most of my time on shore shooting birds, and practising the skinning of them so that when I meet any specimens that I wish to save I can proceed to do it in something of a businesslike way.

Through the kindness of our worthy Captain which it has been my good fortune to get under, I got introduced to almost all the people of note on this Island. They look upon this being the pleasantest time of all the year when the north-west ship is here (as they call them), so the whole country turns out and comes to see the Captain and the Ship, and they never failed to ask me to go along with the Captain to see them, which kindness from strangers is not often to be met with. I sometimes went.

We were one night at the Rev C. Clouston's. He is very fond of Botany and appears to know the plants of Orkney pretty well. On another occasion we made a visit to Dr Watts at a place called Skaill. There I found some ladies very fond of Algae of which they had some good specimens, but many of them without names which they were unable to find from any person, they not having anything like a complete work on that class of plants. When they heard what mission I was going to America on, they thought they would get them all named from me but I was ashamed to say that I knew nothing about them.

The Botany of this island does not present many objects of interest. The only plants that came under my notice as being new to me in their native localities were *Primula Scotica*, *Scilla verna*, *Plantago setacea*. I made the ascent of the Hill of Hoy, it being the highest on the Island. I saw many of the plants common on the higher mountains of the mainland of Scotland, such as *Saxifraga oppositifolia*.

I must give you my sincere thanks for your kind letter. I am quite satisfied with the arrangements you have made with regard to my money matters, and I trust that I will be able to be guided by a right mind to lay it out to the best advantage for the promotion of the end in lieu, not making more expenditure than what is absolutely necessary for the prosecution of my journey, but at the same time to save a little, taking care not to go in a way that there will be danger in losing the whole.

I need add no more at this time. The next you will receive from me, God willing, will be from Hudson's Bay. We have now got all ready to start and have been so for some days, but until the wind changes from the west we can't get out of this Hoy Sound. We have got on board at this place 55 young men going out to the service, and 23 pensioners and their families which joined us at London make up all our emigrants. The only cabin passenger besides myself is a young man going to Red River as a teacher, so we are as comfortable as any person could desire.

I remain, Sir,
Your Ever–Obedient Servant,
John Jeffrey

Journal: Setting sail, 3 July 1850

At last, the winds blew in our favour this morning, and we began our voyage before dawn, our way lit by a pale and waning crescent moon. The tide rushed us across Graemsay Sound, and I bid a quiet farewell to the Hill of Hoy which I could make out only by the way in which its bulk obscured the fading stars.

I observed the sailors at work for many hours, as there seemed a great deal to be done on account of some challenging navigation, requiring regular sounding, and attending to the strong currents. When we had made some distance from the islands, the Old Man of Hoy came into view on our port side, the column standing proudly above the nearby cliffs. A fellow passenger informed me it was 450 feet in height. Even from our distance, I could see it was almost completely obscured by seabirds, while Atlantic rollers crashed and foamed at its base. From this far out, it is evident that the whole islands rise from the ocean bed as a single great mountain. Our soundings proved this, with the depth quickly dropping to 30 fathoms only a short distance from the shore.

During the evening meal, Captain Herd told us that this is no less than his 11th crossing to the Americas, both with this ship and others before her. After we'd all enjoyed a measure of rum, he shared the story of this being the second ship of the same name operated by the HBC, the first being lost to an iceberg. I had the advantage of knowing this before, thanks to the cheerful sailor at Gravesend. Some companions seemed quite put out by the account. I quite hope to see an iceberg; it must be a marvellous sight.

Journal: Atlantic Ocean, 8 July 1850

We are now completely at sea, there being no land visible. The swell is beyond anything I have experienced so far, though the officers tell us we are experiencing a favourable crossing.

I learned much today from Mr Starr, who showed me how he charts our route by shooting the sun at midday, and the North Star or moon at night, by way of a sextant and the celestial tables. Apparently, HBC ships always keep within the 56th and 60th parallels, at least as much as they are allowed by the wind and seas, and occasional ice. My own box sextant works by the same method but in a design that I can carry about my person. Mr Starr was most interested in its design, being the first of this type he had seen that includes a telescope.

He told me we should expect to travel some 60 nautical miles each day, meaning we may reach Cape Farewell off Greenland – our near-halfway point – in the span of about two weeks.

Some of us have had great success in catching mackerel on a line; they seem almost eager to be caught. One of the sailors showed us how to snap their necks by placing a finger in their mouths, and pulling back against the thumb, but only after watching us flounder terribly, much like our first few fish. Being a fish best eaten very fresh, the galley like to serve them the same day, simply fried with a portion of greens (while we have them in our stores).

Journal: Cape Farewell, 22 July 1850

59° 46' 45" N

We passed Cape Farewell this morning, the southernmost tip of Greenland, and our halfway point. There was a great quantity of sea ice near her shore, so we kept a good distance. With the aid of a telescope belonging to one of the officers, I was afforded a good view of this first land since we left the Orkneys. Stripes in the headland's rocks gave the impression of a layered dessert cake, but they were leaning to the sea, suggesting that the whole landmass was sliding off a cake stand.

This is the point at which our route diverges from the passage of Sir John Franklin, whose hardships must only have increased from here as he headed onwards into the frozen north.

I have continued to busy myself by improving my navigation skills, to which end Mr Starr is always most encouraging. We have taken to sighting independently with our own instruments, then exchanging them and repeating the exercise before comparing our findings. We have found that my little instrument fares very well. And so I have busied myself by becoming, by default, an assistant navigator of sorts, though I am not trusted to work in isolation.

I recorded a sea temperature of 37° at this place.

Journal: Iceberg, 31 July 1850

61° 15' 23" N, 56° 37' 35" W

Today, we sighted a huge floating iceberg that brought almost everyone up on deck. It was not the first we've seen, but certainly the largest by some measure, being certainly much taller than our main mast. Beyond this, it was hard to ascertain its real size, as there was nothing other by which its scale could be judged except a lone petrel. We kept our distance, as I'm told they can be even larger below the waves than above, and a great danger to ships who venture too close.

Mr Starr believes that I am becoming quite competent with the sextant, and I often stand with him on the bridge deck. Our current position is the most northerly we have sailed so far.

I recorded a sea temperature of 34° at this place, thus only two degrees above freezing.

Journal: Land ahoy, 5 August 1850

Every one of us has known that land would soon be sighted,

and a constant watch has been kept. At last, this afternoon, a great shout of 'Land ahoy!' brought us all to the deck. It was a relief to find land at last, even though all we could see, without the advantage of the crow's nest and a telescope, was a thick fog bank. Not long after, we began to fall in with more and more ice blocks, becoming larger in size to the point where the officers had to navigate around them. Occasionally, we did still strike some, as there were so many, and it would make us all stagger on our feet, while the ship herself shuddered so much at times that her bell rang. Even though we all now have our sea legs, I confess it was unsettling.

The land itself we gaze upon is Resolution Island, and behind it is the much larger Baffin Island. During the day, both became more visible through the sea mists.

Until today, not much has happened of note. Since the large iceberg noted in my last entry we saw no more of such a size. Beyond practising with the sextant and catching mackerel, I have busied myself reading again some of the papers given to me by Dr Lindley. The sea temperature has remained very close to freezing.

Journal: Hudson Strait, 7 August 1850

After sighting land, we navigated towards Cape Warwick, on the southern tip of Resolution Island, whose great landmass marks the northern entrance to the Hudson Strait. It was visible from at least 30 miles distant, and as we approached, a great wind filled our sails and cleared the fogs. The cliff marking the cape rises dramatically from the sea, its curious red hue made even more resplendent by the setting sun.

Mr Starr says the central channel of the strait is always ice-free, but for eight months of the year it is quite impassable on account of its rapid ice flows. In the past, several HBC ships were lost when they arrived too early in the year, even in July, as some blocks of ice are so large they will destroy a ship's hull. All manner of chains, cables, hooks and axes are on our deck, ready to tackle any ice which might threaten us. The other evening, the captain told us that one year, a HBC ship found it impossible to reach the western shore due to unfavourable winds, tide and ice, and returned all the way to Britain with its full cargo of people, commodities and mail. I can only imagine the frustration of those unfortunate souls on board.

In the strait, we have seen several schools of white whales, the first I have ever witnessed with my own eyes. I have found myself watching them for several hours, if I could find a place to stand away from the wind (for it has been bitterly cold). Even though they are enormous beasts, I sense them to be gentle in nature. They have paid us no attention and seemed content to play about on the surface, and even sun themselves for a time. Sometimes, they are apt to slam their tails on the surface so that an eruption of spray is sent up, and a great boom echoes across the waves. Were I on a smaller boat, I may not think so well about their gentle nature.

Mr Starr has said that the *Prince of Wales* must start her passage home by early September, otherwise the extreme of the cold will turn her sails to stone, her blocks to rocks, and her ropes to bolts. It reminded me of those poor souls with Sir John Franklin, and surely the impossibility of surviving such conditions should they have found themselves delayed further north than this place. I pray that God is merciful to their poor souls.

Journal: At anchor, 12 August 1850

57° 0' 18" N

We are at anchorage, at the mouth of the Hayes River, about 7 miles from York Factory. On the request of the captain, Mr Starr led the crew in some prayers. Afterwards, their joyous singing must surely have brought cheer to God, unless he happened to listen to the words.

The shore of Rupert's Land was, I must admit, an

uninteresting sight through the telescope, comprising only pale sand and low-lying dark-green swamp, and overall looking rather desolate. Knowing what lay far beyond, at least the scale of the mountains to be crossed and the distance to be travelled, only increased my keenness to begin in earnest the land expedition.

Our passage here has been a little under six weeks, which I'm told is very fair for the 2,600 nautical miles we've sailed from the Orkneys. I've been surprised by the sturdiness of my sea legs, and in the diversity of activities and interests one can find when sailing so long a voyage. I quite fancy that if I were not elsewhere employed, I might be tempted to serve on a ship such as this.

Alerted of our arrival by our signal gun, the HBC chief trader – a man named MacTavish – came in a schooner from York Factory to greet us and collect our despatches. I was pleased to be invited ashore by Mr MacTavish, along with the captain and some others. While we waited for the captain to finish his duties on board the *Prince of Wales*, I spoke a little with the steersman. He has lived all his life in this place and delighted in regaling us greenhorns with many a tale. Most interesting of all to me was a great ball of pemmican he carried, of which I had heard much, but never seen. It looked unappealing, being made up largely of fat, but the small morsel I was offered was not so bad to the taste. He told me his was a superior pemmican, being as it contained elk meat with saskatoon berries (I do not yet know this plant).

Later this day we sat for dinner with Mr Heartgreve, the chief factor. Much interest was shown in my expedition. I cannot express enough the simple joy of eating fresh-baked bread with butter and greens after being so long afloat.

Journal: American bush, 13 August 1850

For my first full day on American soil I resolved to explore the locality and take in its nature. Were it not for the fact that I was on land and had a belly full of fresh food, the misery of the place may have been too much. There are so many mosquitoes here; at times they are worse than the Scottish midge, forming clouds around your head and of want of your blood. Underfoot the bush is very wet across the whole place, making going difficult, although the trees seem to be thriving.

The main tree here is *Larix Americana* which is much smaller than the larch we have in Britain, but its stature here is greater than any other species about. The tallest I measured was 30 feet. It appears to grow like birch, being the first to invade new territory, undeterred by even the wettest swamp. The Indians call it tamarack, and I'm told it is the wood of choice for making snowshoes.

I looked a little for beetles but I confess I had little interest in them today.

My spirits were lifted by the Arctic raspberry (*Rubus arcticus*), upon whose fresh fruits I feasted all day.

Abies rubra
Salix Sp.
Alnus serrulatus
Betula nana
Ledum palustris and *Latifolium*
Ribes Hudsoniana and *rubra* and *nigra*
Vaccinum frondosum
Viburnum educe
Empetrum rubric
Arcotapylos ursa
Pyrola uniflora and *rotundifolia*
Rubus arcticus
Cypripedium candidum
Smilicina borealia
Ranunculus Sp.
Primula farinose
Pulmonary paniculata

Journal: York Factory, 14 August 1850

I feel quite sick in the stomach with news just received, and only judge myself foolish that I spent all of yesterday losing blood while chasing sodden trees. The regular transcontinental Brigade – which I was told would take me from this coast all the way to the west coast – has left this place already, being always scheduled for departure in July. The only Brigades that will travel onwards with the contents of the *Prince of Wales* – both people and goods – are those which go as far as various internal trading posts, these being known as the District Brigades. This means that I must wait the best part of one year at this place which has little to offer, it being already well explored by so many others before me.

I have met with Mr Heartgreve and he has reassured me. I can travel with a District Brigade that serves the Saskatchewan District, which will take me towards the Rocky Mountains, at least as far as they can go before winter sets in. This will allow me to move some considerable distance towards my destination, and it is a great relief that I will be able to leave this place, and not wait so long for the regular Brigade. The only alternative solution would be to proceed with some men of my own in a small party, but the distance being so great, and the dangers so considerable, I think I should instead take advantage of the support the HBC can offer and continue with this District Brigade.

With either case, I prefer to be active than idle.

Journal: York Factory, 15 August 1850

The news of yesterday settled with me today, yet I confess I slept little in the night. I resolved to busy myself with preparations for joining the Saskatchewan District's westbound Autumn Express (as they call it), which leaves within a few days. Our main goal will be Edmonton House, about 1,500 miles distant, but I am told that winter can set in before desired, making Cumberland House the farthest attainable place.

I believe that about 50 of us will make up the Express, covering on average 25 miles each day. We will travel on water with a craft designed for the route this side of the Rocky Mountains, which they call the *York Boat*. I have watched men loading four of these today; bow and stern are pointed and made with thick timbers; they have one small removable mast, a flat bottom with space for eight men to row, and with room for others to sit with goods around them.

My accommodation here is fine and I've been made most welcome. It is a much bigger place than I had imagined, consisting of at least 50 buildings that sprawl across the flat land, small bluffs separating them from the Hayes River. They are all constructed with timber; in the past, those built with stone succumbed to the frozen soils, which heave in winter. The main place is handsome, consisting of buildings three storeys high, which together form two squares. Within it is the main depot where provisions are secured by travellers and immigrants, but most of the building provides accommodation for those working with the HBC.

I now have come across a few of the Indians, who I find distracting. Often their brown skin is tattooed and they have faces which, I confess, fascinate me. Many wear buffalo robes with the fur showing outward. I'm told that when reversed they are the best sort for deep winter cold. I have purchased tea and tobacco, as I'm advised this is the best currency with which to pay the Indians while in the interior.

I came across a kitchen where pemmican was being made up. Sacks full of the saskatoon berries allowed me to see that it is not unlike the Scottish blaeberry *Vaccinium myrtillus*, only larger. Apparently, only the best sort of pemmican includes this fruit, as it helps preserve the meat and improves the overall flavour. They were making it with dried buffalo meat which was pounded into a powder before being mixed with equal parts of fat, to which the berries were then added.

Cakes of pemmican are parcelled in hide containers that are then sealed with tallow. The stench of the place was most foul: I can smell it still on my clothes, even as I write hours later.

All my provisions and equipment are now parcelled in several 90 lb units, as this is the standard by which all goods are transported here. I came across the beaver fur press near the stores, where pelts are pressed into bales, also of 90 lb.

I will not be sorry to leave here, as it is very barren, and most surely a very hard place to exist with much comfort, let alone any pleasure. When it rains, which is very often, there is little for shelter and the mud underfoot is most disagreeable.

Letter started to Prof Balfour to send before I depart.

Letter: John Jeffrey to Professor Balfour †

York Factory,
Hudson's Bay
20th August 1850

To Professor Balfour

Sir,

You will see by this that I am on the continent of America, thanks be to our great protector for all his goodness towards us, as I have enjoyed good health since I left Scotland.

Passage across the Atlantic through the Straits was a very good one. We experienced a large proportion of fall winds, but on the other hand we made that up thanks to Hudson's Straits being so clear of ice. The captain informed me that he has never passed through H. Straits for the last 16 years and met with so little obstruction. They are generally beset in it for days and sometimes for weeks. This season we never were stuck fast for an hour, but our progress was very much retarded by the ice being formed into ridges, extending from one frozen shore to the other. For near the shore the ice never breaks up, so when we came into contact with those ridges, the ship was put about and kept sailing along the edge of the ice till she came to a place which was considered sufficiently weak for to force her through.

I have kept a journal of the temperature and all other little incidents that occurred to me of interest on our passage, but the book is not half full so I shall not send it at this time, as it contains nothing of much interest to anyone.

We arrived at the Anchorage at the mouth of the Hayes River on which York factory is situated on Monday the 12th inst. As soon as the ship was discovered from the Factory, Chief Trader MacTavish came down the river in a small boat to take the despatches on shore. This gentleman kindly offered me a passage onshore along with him which I was glad to accept, the Factory being about 7 miles distant from the ship's anchorage.

I was very kindly received by I. Heartgreve Esq., Chief Factor at this establishment. As far as the building of York Factory is concerned, it is a pretty place. The houses are arranged so as to form two squares. The front one is the store of goods for supplying the country on this side of the Rocky Mountains; likewise the storerooms for their furs, and what they call the Summer Houses. This is accommodation for the officers when they congregate, as they do at this season, each trader bringing a fleet of boats with their furs, taking from the ships a supply of goods to serve them for one year's consumption. The back square has the dwelling houses of the people connected with the establishment.

On the 13th I made a day's excursion into the bush here to see what I could find, but unfortunately I was only rewarded by a good wetting and a desperate attack of the plague of this country: the mosquitoes. They do annoy a person very much. The country round here is very low, only 20 feet above the level of the bay, and very flat, covered with an almost impenetrable thicket of small brush, the ground being so soft that you may on walking almost calculate on plunging up to the knee with every step. The woods that compose the growth of the swamps are *Larix Americana*, towering up, its head above everything else, covered with long white moss which gives it a very old and stunted appearance. The tallest of the *Larix* does not exceed much more than 30 feet. Next comes *Abies rubra* – they are quite outstripped by the *Larix* in stature, 20 feet being their greatest height. I have seen several not more than 3 feet and completely covered with cones. Next to them comes the Salix of several different species. Then comes *Alnus serrulatus, Betula nana, Ledum palustris, L. Latifolium, Ribes Hudsoniana* and *rubra* and *nigra, Vaccinum frondosum, Viburnum educe, Empetrum rubric, Arcotapylos ursa, Pyrola uniflora* and *rotundifolia. Rubus arcticus* fruit – now ripe, they form one of the finest productions of Hudson's Bay in the way of dessert. The other plants that occur are *Cypripedium candidum, Smilicina borealia,* with a good many species of Ranunculus, none of them of much consequence, such as *brevicalis* and *Borealis. Primula farinose* is here in great quantities. *Pulmonary paniculata* is one of the showiest plants that I have come across, and I think from the nature of the country I need not expect much until I penetrate a little further into the interior. I must just proceed by rule of thumb, as I could find no American Flora when I was in London. When I meet anything that I don't know and have not seen in Britain, I will endeavour to procure seeds of it if possible, and if you find such things are not worth distribution, they can be cast aside.

I expected to have had something in the way of beetles to send home by the Ship but it will be out of my power. They are very scarce here. I have picked a good number but not so many as would repay for Carriage.

I am to proceed for the interior tomorrow. It is a matter of doubt whether I can get further than Cumberland House this fall or not. If it is possible, I shall make as far as Edmonton House. I have got provisions for my winter keep, likewise some tea and tobacco for purchasing the assistance of the Indians. I have bought as much except what I may be able to kill with my gun as should take me to Fort Vancouver. Mr Heartgreve made me do this, as it is much cheaper here than in the interior of the country and sometimes it can't be got. I have likewise got a small tent and blankets, indeed I had to purchase everything that I will require for wintering on. I purchased in Stromness, Orkney all the winter clothing that I shall want to enable me to do that. The Hudson's Bay Company's Agent there paid 2 pounds for me, but that being spent on under clothing you will deduct it from my wages.

If I cross the mountains with the regular Brigade, that would not be till about this time next year, but the question is this: whether I can find it practicable to travel by myself accompanied by one or two for assistance. From what I learn from the gentleman here the Indians on the route are by no means troublesome. If I can find a way to do this, as far as my own judgement goes I think that this will be by far the most wise plan of proceeding, for if I stayed for the regular Brigade I would lose the best part of the season. What makes this to be avoided if possible is the little chance of finding anything worth spending my time here for. This side has been so ransacked by Drummond, Douglas and Sir W. Hooker's Collector that he had out in 1846; he was two years on this side and found nothing. There is one of the officers here of the Fort at which he made his headquarters, and he informs me that he made nothing to recompense him the whole season that he lived with him. I have a good portion of this season before me yet, so during that time I must make every effort to procure what I can. After I get to my winter quarters, I will be more in a position to devise that plan for my procedure as I may think most likely to forward the object in view. During winter, birds, skins and any other object of Natural History that I can collect must take my attention.

Any letter of instruction to me that is forwarded to the care of E. Lewis Esq., Chief Factor, Cumberland House, will find me. If I get beyond that this season, I will give him instructions where to forward it so as to find me.

I remain, Sir,

Your very Obedient Servant,

John Jeffrey

Journal: Heading west, 20 August 1850

My transcontinental journey is finally underway, in the company of 47 others, travelling with the Autumn Express. We left one day earlier than I had been told I must prepare for, but by all accounts, all preparations and persons were ready by this morning, including myself. I admit that I was keen to leave York Factory and excited at the prospect of beginning this stage of the expedition, even though my stomach has been turning at the thought of the adventures ahead. I have heard so many tales about the hardships we will face for the next 40 days or more; the power of the rapids, the Herculean toil of portaging, the hours of paddling, the many large beasts that might lie in wait, and more besides. I slept very little, and I am convinced the mosquitoes learned that I would soon be on my way, and came in hordes for a final meal as I tossed and turned in my bed.

We have travelled all day up the mouth of the Hayes River, the tide and winds favouring us. The river is wide here and its current languid. No sooner had we left York Factory than a forest of pines crowded the river on either side. We have had no need to leave the main channel all day, meaning I've had few opportunities for looking at the trees in detail, though they look to be the same sort as before. About 10 miles from York Factory we halted to attend to an unbalanced boat. I took the opportunity to collect five clusters of immature cones of *Abies Nigra* (numbering 60 cones in all) from a diminutive tree just 7 feet high.

There are 11 of us in our York boat, made up mostly of company men who are familiar with the territory, being experienced traders or Brigade men. The only others inexperienced like me are two men who keep strangely close to each other and say little (I know not their business), and a kindly Irish woman who prepares the food for all of us. The steersman is a friendly fellow named Douglas – appropriately for the start of my land expedition – though he knows nothing at all of the names of plants. He is a veteran Brigade member who appears very hardy. He is the sort whose age is impossible to judge, but he says he has made this journey to Edmonton House and back twice each year for the last 12 years. He is never without a tobacco pipe in his mouth, even while undertaking a rigorous manual task.

We travelled mostly under sail, occasionally using the oars, but only when the current was too strong, or where the high banks or trees lulled the wind. The conditions being so favourable most of the day, until the rain set in, we travelled for more than 10 hours to reach our first camp, which we've made on a small island.

I'm writing by candlelight from the small tent I purchased at York Factory. The rain is drumming on the canvas over my head, and our pitiful cooking fire is quite extinguished (but not before I stole a glowing coal to smoke out my tent interior with a view to exterminating the bloodsuckers). Speaking of the mosquitoes, it seems they are mostly seeking shelter in the trees, which is a merciful relief to us all.

After the excitement I felt at the beginning of this journey, this languid day has seemed a damp squib. It has done little to ease my concerns about the hardships which lie ahead, and I cannot shake from my mind the well-known saying – of the calm before a storm.

~*~

Bald eagle
Loon
Otter
Beaver
Moose
Porcupine
Wolf (tracks only)
Grizzly bear (tracks only)

Journal: Swampy Lake, 12 September 1850

This place is well named, being surrounded on all sides by very wet ground. The mosquitoes here are the worst we've encountered.

Since my last account, we travelled in a south-westerly direction, and increasingly met with rapids, which mile by mile have become more arduous. Some of the rapids on the Hayes we were not able to ascend without unloading the boats, then poling. For this we used very stout 10-foot-long wooden poles, which have a metal ferrule for grip on the riverbed, and by this means we moved the York over the riffles and minor rapids. On reaching the Hills River, the rapids became too vigorous for poling. All of us, other than Douglas and one of the strongest HBC brigademen – always it seems, an Orcadian – would remain in the boat to pole, while the rest of our company portage half the cargo along the bank so that the boat is made lighter. So many fallen trees make this hazardous and exhausting, and every part is wet and slippery. Then sometimes we must return to the bottom again to help haul the boats up the rapids, by means of ropes to which we are harnessed; a method they call tracking. Many days it has been very hard work, and one day we made only 2 miles at most, portaging and tracking almost all that distance.

My hands are quite raw from so much rough work, having become better suited, since I left Edinburgh, to the work of office clerk than gardener. My feet fare worse, on account of being always wet. Douglas told me to dry them while I was resting in the boat, and this advice I have heeded in recent days, to good effect, though there is little skin on my soles left intact.

I remember clearly the instruction from the Gentleman of the Oregon Botanical Association that, as the progress would be quite slow, that I could avail myself of the time to make plant collections at every opportunity. There was never any suggestion that I would be a necessary cog in the engine of the Express. I think, perhaps, that some had imagined I might be carried from place to place in a sedan chair by native servants!

For about 40 miles, we traversed at least a dozen major rapids; all of them Douglas has known personally, describing them in great detail before we could even see them. I cannot recall the names of all of them, but they were well named, among them The Shield, Rocky Launcher and the Devil's Landing Place. None have succeeded in extinguishing his pipe – whatever the degree of their raging torrent – which I think he must wedge firmly between his few remaining teeth. The last rapids, at the end of this terrible section, they call Dramstone Falls. As tradition dictates on reaching this place, in the evening we all partook in a little Irish whiskey, and toasted Douglas and the other voyageurs, and ourselves, on reaching this milestone.

Appropriately, our encampment is on Sail Island, not far from Dramstone Falls. The mast and sail, being recently of no use, have been stowed for many days, but tomorrow on this small lake (about 9 miles in length), we hope the wind will help us make rapid progress, and perhaps we may all recover some strength. Even bringing my pen to work has been a hardship that I could not overcome, on account of the exhaustion in my arms and shoulders, hence the void in this account.

Two men in my York are shirking some of the work and are unpopular among the rest of us. Even the Métis women, who I have watched in the other boats, are of more help to those crews, being excellent paddlers, and always uncomplaining. One of these men – who I will not name – is a feeble sort; I think a puff of Rupert's wind might render him a spent dandelion pappus at any moment. The other is well built, yet arrogant and lazy; I have quietly named him Sugg. The other evening, Miss Lizzy, our cook, rapped him on the knuckles with her wooden spoon for dipping his finger in the stew she was busily preparing for us – she now wears a black eye.

Collected about 100 immature green cones of *Pinus Banksiana* from the Hill River.

Journal: Knee Lake, 13 September 1850

55° 12' 14" N

Sailing across Swampy Lake was a simple, but all too short, pleasure. There followed a 10-mile stretch of the Jack Tent River which had us portaging four times. We've reached Knee Lake, which is very large, and named on account of a bend along its leg. Our encampment is at its far eastern end, and tomorrow we all look forward – given a fair wind – to the hoisting of our sail again.

Loons are calling as I write; like aquatic owls. They only add to the eeriness of this lonely place.

Journal: Oxford House, 15 September 1850

54° 56' 54" N

We have made good time to reach this place, and are now able to resupply ourselves from the HBC stores, and enjoy a little comfort. We are to rest here for two nights.

To make up my account before now, after sailing some 20 comfortable miles from our last encampment, we approached the 'knee' of the island of that name, where a small island only just rises above the lake, and is thickly covered with scrub. One of the voyageurs knew that I had a compass and encouraged me to take it out and look at it. I was astounded to find it totally without purpose. The needle agitated randomly across all quarters before finally swinging its north point firmly southwards in the direction of the island! At first I thought it must be damaged, but when he laughed I realised he had known of this effect all the while. It is called Magnetic Island for its curious effect on a compass. I was keen to stand on it to see what other effects there may be, and may even have persuaded Douglas to allow me that, only for him to spot a grizzly bear who was evidently waiting for us to join him for dinner. This is the first bear I've seen, and I found the beast even more imposing than I had imagined from all the tales I'd heard. He held his long nose aloft, pointing it towards our boat, and looked as though he was already tasting us.

The wind being against us, we rowed the last 4 miles, passing west of the knee before we left the lake, and once again had to ascend a steep section of the Hayes, which here they also call the Trout River. Along its 12-mile length we had to make four portages. At one, called Knife Rapids, we were made to empty almost all our York before tracking upstream, otherwise the vicious gneiss pebbles would slice open our hull (much like they did our feet). We camped near there for one night.

A serious confrontation between Douglas and Sugg occurred that evening, which would surely have come to blows if that lazy fellow had not retreated with no shame for his languidity. I believe I may not have been alone in imagining the banquet for the grizzly, had we left him behind on Magnetic Island.

Along one portage during the day, Douglas came across some wild onions, and for our evening meal he added them to pemmican, together with flour and water, to make a stew he called Rubaboo. There was no space for tents at our encampment near the Knife Rapids, and being a clear night, and fresh enough to dissuade mosquitoes, we slept under our coats. Thanks to a full stomach and overall fatigue, I slept soundly, despite the roar of the falls. Sugg was notably absent for the meal, appearing again sometime during the night, so that he was sleeping next to us when we rose before dawn.

Here at Oxford House, I intend to take full advantage of our one day of rest, but I will endeavour to explore the surrounding forest a little. There are many Indians here, trading goods and seeking employment of one form or another; most of them herald from a tribe called the Cree. Douglas explained how carrying a pipe signifies peaceful intentions among them, which is maybe why he seems quite at ease in their company. I find them so different to any people I've met before that I catch myself looking too hard, and I confess that I'm self-conscious in their presence. On their part, without exception, they tend to look straight at you with no timidity, which lends them an air of quiet superiority.

Specimen: *Picea* Sp., 15 September 1850 †

Oxford House. Tree 50 feet high, 9 inches diameter. Collected 54 cones.

Specimens: Collections from Oxford House, 19 September 1850 †

Five clusters of cones of Abies Rubra *(numbering 54 cones) from a tree 50 feet high, 9 inches in diameter.*

Three clusters of cones of Abies Alba *(numbering 22 cones) from a tree 100 feet high and 18 inches in diameter.*

Journal: Norway House, 21 September 1850

53° 59' 25" N

Leaving Oxford House and its modest creature comforts

behind, we sailed 15 miles westwards across Oxford Lake, before ascending the Hayes River again. The country here is more gentle, and the only barrier to progress an occasional beaver dam.

We reached eventually a place well known and named Painted Stone, where the Hayes meets the Echimamish River, both running close and parallel to each other, and flowing eastwards. We had only to take 20 paces to pass from one stream to the other, before continuing westward upstream along the Echimamish. This river – in fact little more than a stream – had little discernible current for its entire 40-mile length. It was often narrow and deep, made dark by the peat, and full of leeches which bothered me only when they chose my softest fleshy parts. Others, in particular Sugg, have been greatly vexed by them, although in his case, I have wondered whether they find any sustenance in his blood. It was apparent they were not the only creatures after his blood, judging by the angry cheek and fattened lip he sported in camp that evening. I noticed Douglas massaging his knuckles while we sat talking round the fire, though he said nothing of it, nor did I probe!

We passed through many small lakes, and ponds made by beavers, all of little note except for a very long portage between the shallow, reed-ridden Max Lake and its larger sister, Logan Lake. This strange river came to an end after Hairy Lake, where it joined the River Nelson.

It was an unusual sensation, travelling downstream with a discernible current, and we met no rapids at all on the Nelson until we reached the impressive Sea River Falls. Here the river drops 7 feet and is very turbulent, creating thunderous curling waves; the sort that hold fast to boat and man, never to release them. It was too perilous to continue on the water, but the portage was mercifully short.

From there it was an easy paddle to Little Playgreen Lake, whose rough waters beckoned us finally towards Norway House.

The house itself is set a little back from the shore, hidden partly by a rocky headland, and it was a great relief to see its white-painted walls shining brightly in front of the dark forest of jack pine. It is a busy place, being the administrative centre for the HBC, with goods of all sorts being traded and jobs bartered by many people, with more milling about.

I've been relieved to eat some fresh vegetables, including potatoes, and to wear dry socks, though my boots remain a little damp.

Journal: Mouth of the Saskatchewan River, 28 September 1850

With the weather set fair, the Express continued on from Norway House on 26 September, with all letters despatched and trading completed. After 25 miles, we reached the northern shore of Lake Winnipeg, which is the largest body of water I've seen since Hudson's Bay. It is more an inland sea than a lake, and had I been the first explorer to reach its shores, I may have believed it to be the end of the continent, on account of the horizon stretching ahead with no land in sight.

I believe we were all very much relieved to learn on reaching this place that the malingering Sugg and his companion had reached their final destination, and that we would no longer have to tolerate them in our York. Not a single word of farewell was imparted to either man, and at our last breakfast together I said nothing when I watched Lizzy spit in Sugg's porridge one last time.

In their place we have been joined by a young Indian – perhaps of similar age to me, but it is difficult to be sure – and we found ourselves sitting together. We found much to talk about during the journey. Originating from the Woodland Cree, he is named Wahiya, which he told me proudly means 'far away'. He has a handsome face with long dark hair, tied with colourful braids. Some Indians dress as the voyageurs, but this man chooses to dress in his traditional clothes. His trousers are not made in one piece, instead consisting of a breechcloth tucked front to back between his legs, and with two separate leggings. His jacket has long sleeves, decorated with tassels and a few beads. On his feet he wears simple moccasins. All his garments are made from the softest deerskin.

Douglas had warned us that on reaching Lake Winnipeg we would experience a tough section ahead, even with the winds in our favour. We soon found that he had not exaggerated his notice to any degree. We sailed westwards for 40 miles, day and night, without pause, as there was nowhere to land, the waves crashing against an unbroken stretch of high cliffs all that distance. Wahiya and I matched each other on the oars, sometimes for several hours at a time. I believe I am already much stronger in physique, and may yet make a competent voyageur.

We eventually found shelter in Limestone Bay, near the lake's north-west corner, at 53° 46' 3" N. The shores of the lake afford only a scant growth of diminutive *Coniferae*, and they offered us little protection. We therefore portaged across a narrow spit to reach behind it, and there, protected from the relentless south-easterly, we made our encampment. None of our company had much energy to cook, and unusually we ate raw pemmican, though we had a little remaining fresh bread that made it somewhat more tolerable.

Next day, we took advantage of the shelter in this bay and sailed in lee of the spit, before covering another 40 miles across the main lake body, reaching anchorage in the mouth of the Saskatchewan River. Here, we have paused for two days.

Journal: Grand Rapids, 30 September 1850

53° 10' 49" N

Even though my body suffered from a deep fatigue, my mind had been well prepared by Douglas, and the others who are experienced voyageurs, for the most significant impediment to our hardy Express. The appropriately named Grand Rapids were the last major obstacle before we reach Cumberland House (now just 160 miles distant). The rapids extend some 3 miles, and we had to make an ascent of the River Saskatchewan as it falls 75 vertical feet towards Lake Winnipeg.

We left our encampment at three o'clock in the morning, and only succeeded in reaching the top of the falls well after nightfall, all this time engaged in significant exertion. I've heard that often the portage can take two days. Much of today, I was tracking immediately behind Wahiya, and I've never witnessed a man toil so hard. The HBC has created a road to help the men with tracking the Yorks, and the portaging of all the usual provisions. It proved to be much needed by us all in climbing this considerable obstacle. It is difficult to conceive how much effort would have been required before it was here.

Afterward, Wahiya found the energy to raise our campfire this evening, and within the hour returned with two sturgeon from Cedar Lake (I was fascinated by their bony plates), whose flesh he shared among those from our boat and some others. I am very impressed by this man.

Specimen: *Larix Pendula*, Grand Rapids, 1 October 1850 †

Nine clusters of cones of Larix Pendula *(very small cones) from a tree 18 feet high, and branches very pendulous, taken on the banks of the River Saskatchewan near the Grand Rapids. Collected 1st October.*

Journal: Cumberland House, 6 October 1850

53° 56' 29" N

We started this, our last leg before Cumberland House, early on the morning following the Grand Rapids, hoping to benefit from a friendsome wind. We made fast progress north-west across Cedar Lake. After breakfasting at its source, we continued – by pole and sometimes by tracking – up the Saskatchewan towards Muddy Lake, near where we made our encampment.

The next day the river narrowed and its bed changed quite suddenly from bedrock to mud, the banks becoming encroached by willow and alder. We spent the whole day fighting the brush and a fast current, finally sleeping for an uncomfortable short night in our boats, on account of the narrowness of the channel.

The third day we reached The Pas, at the confluence of the Pasquia River, near an Indian settlement. This place sits on a small rise above the surrounding land, which is very flat. We enjoyed a restful encampment, made memorable by a plentiful catch of pike and small white fish which were very abundant in these waters. There followed some tiresome days on the Saskatchewan River, whose rocky and sandy bed twisted and turned in every direction. We eventually made the shores of Cumberland Lake, and the house of the same name from where I now write, early in the morning.

We were welcomed, with much warmth, by Chief Factor Mr Lewis. In the country, however, a winter chill is setting in fast.

Journal: Cumberland House, 11 October 1850

The first snow fell overnight, immediately after our arrival at this house, and the air temperature has since remained below freezing every day. There have been discussions between the Express leader and Mr Lewis as to whether we proceed or not to our final destination. This would be Fort Edmonton, which is 600 miles distant. It is a grave decision, there being no midway place at which we could reside for the worst part of winter, and even turning back might be impracticable.

I think it now unlikely that we will proceed, as the rivers will soon become impassable in the Yorks; the channels will soon be frozen, while their icy banks will make tracking intolerable.

I talked at some length with Douglas, who has suggested that if I wish to keep moving, I should join with the Winter Packet. This is named after a leather packet containing letters and other important communications between HBC trading posts. A hardy group of men carries this relatively lightweight cargo, travelling on foot and with dogs from York Factory, reaching this place sometime in the middle of winter. It then continues on to the Rockies, reaching the Pacific coast in the summer. Douglas offered me a warning that this option is not for the faint-hearted, being tougher than any part of our journey so far, but I believe he thinks highly of my hardiness by suggesting this option to me.

Journal: Cumberland House, 13 October 1850

The decision has been made to halt the Express. The lake is wearing a skirt of ice almost thick enough to stand my weight.

I have made up my mind to join the Winter Packet when it reaches this place. I must remain here meanwhile, perhaps for another two months. I was heartened by the news that Wahiya intends to join this group. I consider him a friend, and a worthy companion.

Journal: Cumberland House, 1 November 1850

I have little reason for making an entry, other than that today marks the start of November. Winter's grasp is now fast around this place. The ground is everywhere thick with snow, the lake frozen and often gracing huge flocks of skating geese. Sadly, they are so timorous I cannot get close with my gun. In the swamps – which is most of the land about – there is generous cover, and there, I have shot plenty of game.

I attend church regularly, and many of the Indians seem to be avid devotees. Only once have I seen Wahiya there; and then I think only curiosity attracted him. Last Sunday (27th), there was the baptism of a young Métis girl and a Cree man.

Most days I help teach the children English, and even a little botany. I have learned much from the Indian children about the trees and their uses. They make a tea from the inner bark of many different trees, including the birch and tamarack.

I have busied myself for the span of two weeks making snowshoes with Wahiya. For the frames, we searched carefully for clean stems of tamarack, meaning those free of knots. After being cut to length, these were soaked in water for one day, and then heated in boiling water so that they could be easily bent. When still hot they were bound to shape using babiche, a strong sinew, and then dried for some days near the fire. We made holes in the frames with a bow drill, and through these I learned to weave the fine mesh at the front of the shoe with moose sinew; Wahiya found it amusing to tease me, this normally being a job for the women. We used thicker babiche for the areas which support the feet. On their tips we mounted animal furs, which I am told have a spiritual meaning; but also now we can tell our shoes apart, as mine have rabbit fur. Now they are finished they look very fine; some 4 feet in length and shaped much like a canoe.

Wahiya shared an Indian legend, told to me while we crafted our shoes, which I will repeat here. In the old days, all animals spoke to the Cree. One night a hunter awoke when his snowshoes spoke to him – 'Wake up, wake up!'

They told him that danger was coming and that he must leave quickly. He walked a long way and eventually came to a lake. His legs were tired, yet still the danger was drawing closer.

'If only I had some otter leggings, then I could continue,' he said.

Then two otters came close by, and he killed them and made himself leggings. They warmed his tired legs and soon he felt no more pain, and was able to escape. And so his life was saved thanks to the otters, and especially thanks to his snowshoes which had first alerted him, then carried him to safety.

With our main task complete, Wahiya showed me how, with the fine tamarack offcuts, the Cree make goose decoys. They were simple to construct, being made of the finer branches and twigs – which now are bare of leaves – bound together with fine sinew. They are made in two pieces, the first being the egg-shaped body, complete with blunt tail. To shape the head and neck, a sheaf of twigs is bound tightly and then split in two, one half becoming the top of the head, the other the throat and bill, before being joined back together to form the curved neck. The hollow in the head part creates a large eye and face, which makes them look very much alive in the snow and ice. We made a 'flock' of half a dozen, and each being slightly different in appearance, they look most natural.

Letter: Oregon Botanical Association to the Subscribers †

Edinburgh
20th November 1850

Sir,

We have had the good fortune to secure the service of Mr Jeffrey, a young Botanist, as Collector, whose high Testimonials, as well as the personal intercourse which several of the Committee had with him, warrant them in anticipating a successful issue to his labours.

Mr Jeffrey has set out under the most favourable auspices. Not only has he been furnished with Credentials from the Foreign Office and the Lords of the Admiralty, which will secure him the assistance of such of Her Majesty's Officers as he may meet with, as well as free transit from place to place along the Western Coast of North America in Her Majesty's vessels; but the Hudson's Bay Company have, in the handsomest manner, accorded their co-operation and assistance, without which the Expedition, in at least one part of its bound, would have been comparatively unfruitful. They have also given Mr Jeffrey a free passage to North America. He sailed from London in their ship the *Prince of Wales* in the beginning of June, and letters have since been received from him, dated 20th August. He was then preparing to prosecute his way across the Continent.

Another service which this Association receives from the Hudson's Bay Company, and which is of great importance, is the free transmission home of their packages of seeds. This secures their being both well taken care of and protected from the damaging influence of exposure to the heat of the climates through which they would have had to pass by Panama, or any other route. The packages of seeds will, on their arrival in this country, be deposited in the warehouses of Hudson's Bay House in London, where they will be examined by Custom-House Officers in presence of the servants of the Company.

Mr Jeffrey has also been kindly supplied by some of the Shareholders with letters to private individuals, and to the Missionary Stations in the Countries through which he is to penetrate, which cannot fail to be productive of much benefit.

The only point on which the Committee are not fully satisfied is the amount of funds subscribed for. The sum already subscribed amounts to L.950, but they are afraid a larger sum needs to be raised to enable them to realise the full value of the arrangements they have made and the assistance they have obtained. It must be obvious that in exploring a country so distant that it takes nearly 12 months to reach, there must be a great waste both of time and means if they should be obliged speedily to recall the Collector. To send him out for only three years gives him little more than one year to explore the district he is sent to.

Looking to the advantageous auspices under which their Collector goes out, the Committee are sure all would deeply regret to see such an excellent opportunity not taken fully advantage of. They have, therefore, had no difficulty in resolving that steps should be taken to secure an increase in their funds. They conceive, also, that this is the proper time to carry out their resolution, that they may know exactly the funds they have to look to, and be able to send out instructions to Mr Jeffrey in the spring, directing him either to return at the end of 1852, or to continue his labours.

With these views, the Committee has taken into consideration the best means of increasing their funds. They are unwilling to increase the number of Shareholders, as by doing so, they would increase the difficulty of dividing the seeds sent home. It has therefore occurred to them that the best mode would be for the present Subscribers to continue their subscriptions for one or two years longer.

Several gentlemen have already intimated their willingness to continue their Subscriptions on this footing; and I am directed to express a hope that you will also do so.

In that case, your second subscription of L.5 a share would become payable in November 1851, and your Third in November 1852.

I have the honour to be,

Sir,

Your most obedient and humble servant,

Andrew Murray, Joint Secretary

Journal: Cumberland House, 3 December 1850

I failed to note the arrival of December. Time has passed slowly in this frozen land. I sincerely wish for the Winter Packet to arrive before long.

A tragedy hit this place one night last week, while we all cowered from a terrible gale. A large jack pine – whose canopy was laden with snow – fell on a house. Such was the howling of the wind yet the muffling of the snow, no one heard the tree fall, and the scene was not discovered until the morning, by which time it was too late. The entire family was crushed or had suffocated. The whole community turned out to mourn; the little coffins of the children, and a tiny baby, upset all of us.

My preparations are complete for onward travel. I have a long buffalo robe for which I bartered with the Indians. It cost me a great deal of tobacco, but I am greatly pleased with it. I also have some mittens and a fur hat, both made from beaver fur, and Indian stockings to keep snow from entering my boots. I had thought the coat I purchased before to be adequate; I now appreciate the wisdom of the Indians who have survived here so long.

I must leave behind some of my belongings, as I will only be able to travel on from here with the most essential items. Mr Lewis tells me he will arrange for the Columbia Brigade to forward my other baggage to Fort Vancouver, when it arrives here in late spring.

Journal: Cumberland House, Christmas Day, 1850

The Winter Packet has still to reach this place. We have suffered very strong winds this last week and the snowdrifts lie waist-deep. The warmest temperature I have recorded this month has been 12°, and more normally it is -4°. It is hard to imagine how any men can reach this place, yet they surely must if they are to be safe at all. The thought that I will join them onwards fills me with some trepidation, although I fancy that my strength and journeying skills are both much improved compared with when I first set out from York Factory. It seems a lifetime ago that I left the *Prince of Wales* and the great Atlantic behind; as to my life in Scotland, that seems altogether another life from a far distant dream.

I am now well used to my snowshoes; without them it is impossible to walk anywhere, other than on the well-trodden paths among the buildings, and even then only if there has been little snowfall in a day. They have proven to be indispensable for Wahiya and I during our hunting excursions.

Some of us shared a goose at dinner – thanks largely to our tamarack decoys – and we enjoyed more dancing than usual to mark this festive day.

DEHISCENCE

1851

SPLITTING AT MATURITY TO
DISPERSE SEEDS

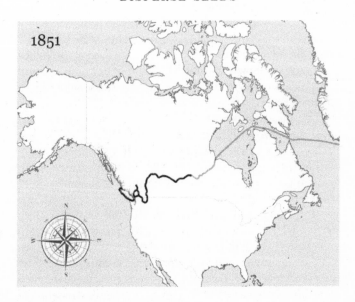

1851

Journal: Cumberland House, 3 January 1851

The Winter Packet arrived just before nightfall, accompanied by many shouts of 'The Winter Packet, the Winter Packet!' which echoed round the settlement. The men with it looked exhausted and much relieved to have reached this place, yet there was much merriment at their arrival and hurried exchange of news. There are six of them in all, split into three teams, each with four magnificent dogs.

Journal: Cumberland House, 4 January 1851

I met with the main guide responsible for the group carrying the Winter Packet. Caleb – he offered only his Christian name – is a giant, standing several inches taller than 6 feet, with a beard so thick it hides most of his face. I fear my purpose was anathema to him, yet Mr Lewis has clearly conveyed the importance of my expedition, as my travel with these men has been agreed. I am to be issued my own toboggan, and four dogs to pull what baggage I have remaining with me. There will be eight of us going on from here, including Wahiya. He knows the track, and will be our main scout.

Round the warmth of the evening fire, with some good food, the men revelled in telling stories about the Winter Packet. Many of these featured everything from starvation to different degrees of hardship, with the men even resorting to eating a dog on occasion. The most gruesome tale of winter travel came from years gone by. It featured two starving Indian women whose lonely trail was discovered by some HBC men, and followed for reasons of concern and charity. Once they were found, the women were given some of the men's precious supplies to sustain them before the men moved on. Later that night, as they slept, the men were brutally attacked with axes by the same women, and murdered for their meagre possessions. I confess that my sleep last night was disrupted by many vivid imaginations.

Journal: Cumberland House, 5 January 1851

I spent some time today with the dogs, attempting to learn from one of the Winter Packet voyageurs how to control them. Commanding 'Marche' to set them going, he made it look a simple task, yet in my hands I found myself picking up an upturned toboggan time and time and again. It was exhausting work, even though the toboggan was empty. The dogs are very strong, and when I rode the toboggan it was a great thrill travelling so fast over the snow, especially once I had learned to lean on turning. I have some new words to use, including 'Haw!' and 'Gee!', for left and right, among the more obvious ones. Getting the dogs to 'Halt!' I find more difficult than getting them to start, unlike all my experience with draft animals at home.

Once or twice I felt Caleb's eyes on me, watching from the shelter of a portico. Even from a distance, their sparkling blue is disconcerting; they seemed to gather the brightness of the snow and focus it on me, piercing me from under the dark shadow of his hood. I do not think he cares so much for me.

The toboggan is designed less to carry men as their baggage, so I must trot or walk behind on snowshoes. The vehicle is made from birch boards 8 inches in width, lashed together with babiche, and overall is some 10 feet in length. All of them are decorated to a degree, some with numerous little bells, which I am told helps to keep spirits high when the going is hard, although I can only imagine they would become tiresome after a while. With Wahiya, I have decorated my toboggan with strips of bright cloth, which also serve to protect those areas most prone to damage.

The dogs are the largest I've seen anywhere, their shoulders reaching almost to my waist. The thickness of their coats is tremendous, making them appear larger still.

They are gentle giants, at least with the men, yet between themselves I have witnessed them fighting viciously for the best scraps of meat.

I believe we are to leave very soon. Supplies of pemmican, potatoes, onions and some other foods, plus a little fresh bread, have been secured for our onward travel. No doubt the Packet itself has also been filled with new correspondence. I considered adding a letter of my own, but there seems little purpose if I am to travel alongside the Packet for so long. Instead, I will write when we reach the next depot, which, God willing, will be Fort Edmonton.

Journal: Fort Edmonton, 25 February 1851

53° 32' 1" N

Our hardy party arrived here yesterday, 50 days after we set out from Cumberland House. This is the longest period during which I've made no written record, it being inconceivable in every respect to make any sort of regular account in my journal.

We traversed about 800 miles, all of which followed the valley of the Saskatchewan River, covering some 15–20 miles each day. Some days, a blizzard made onward travel impossible, and we were forced then to stay where we were and simply attempt to keep ourselves warm and alive.

I have learned how much a fire can mean to a man. On reaching a place to stop for the night, always our first activity was to source branches suitable for the fire – these being large and dead – and ideally still attached to the pines or birches (so they were dry). They would be laid out to form a raft of sorts, 6 feet or more in length, to float on top of the snow. On the raft, finer branches would be stacked and, finally, a handful of dry tinder (taken from the supply all of us carry in our packs). I cannot describe the relief felt when the first lick of flame and puff of smoke is born from the sparks of flint and steel. When the cold is -40° or lower, even the smallest flame brings welcome warmth, and we would sleep with it as near to our feet as possible. We would take turns during the night to keep watch on the fire to keep us all from freezing, and in the morning it would be ready to heat our breakfast.

Meals were most often of pemmican if we had no luck finding fresh game. For a welcome change to Rubaboo, we sometimes fried pemmican with onions and potatoes, at least while we still had them in our supplies, making a satisfying meal they call *Rechaud*. It has been too difficult to fish, now the river is thick with ice. We often set snares made from babiche for rabbits, and sometimes had luck shooting willow ptarmigan, and less often a spruce grouse. The men call the latter the Fool's Hen, on account of its habit of sitting tight in branches, using perfect camouflage until the last moment, before surprising us in a great flurry of wings and snow.

Our usual way to travel would be to have one man out front (often Wahiya), and the sleds would follow one another in a single line, like a train, using the running marks of those in front. The men would always walk or run besides the train, except down some slopes. The dogs are marvellous, and most extraordinary. They would run all day, with a strength beyond comparison in such conditions. At night, once fed, and the squabbles settled, they would sleep together in the snow, kept together by a chain in case they fancied some wild game more than our company. We were entirely reliant upon them for our survival.

Sometimes along the way, we were lucky to reach a small trading post, abandoned for the winter; most usually a small wood cabin used by hunters during the frost-free months. More often, we slept under whatever cover could be found with only our robes around us; a blanket and bed of green branches lay between our bodies and the snow. All of us suffered from cold feet, and Caleb warned us only ever to heat our toes slowly by the heat of the fire. One of the men ignored his advice and his toes went from blue to purple, large blisters forming and causing him great discomfort. Later, both his small toes turned black and he became quite lame, causing Caleb to curse him terribly. I believe the poor man was more afraid of those piercing eyes than he was of the cold, and perhaps he was mercifully distracted, at least in part, from the terrible pain he must have experienced. On my own part, I suffered some minor frostbite, but nothing to slow me. Wahiya seemed least affected among us all; I think his clothes are superior to ours in all respects. He was always happy to be ahead on the trail, leading the way before the dogs.

To mention Caleb again, we have found ourselves an agreeable relationship. I believe that my ability to shoot game has earned his respect, while I have been among the strongest on my feet. Even my mushing became acceptable in time.

Attending the chapel at Fort Edmonton today in the company of the same men, to give thanks for our safe passage, was a strange experience after our shared hardships. It was as if a new light fell on us all, and we behaved like strangers to one another.

Journal: Fort Edmonton, 26 February 1851

I enjoyed some gentle excursions around the fort today. It stands on the left bank of the Saskatchewan River, enjoying a good view over the wider country from its vantage on a modest hill, with small cliffs protecting it from the river.

A wooden palisade forms an irregular barricade around the place, with a small bastion at each turn. Within its walls are some 11 buildings, including several dwelling houses (with a separate one for the Indians), a blacksmith and the chapel. The house of the chief factor, Mr John Rowland, is a wooden building three storeys high. It can be seen from the fields beyond, rising above the 25-foot-high palisade.

Being so long in the wilderness, and accustomed to the extreme cold, I have found it a strange adjustment to living again in a house, and wearing fewer garments to the point of feeling quite naked, even though I still wear several layers.

I found it a great comfort yesterday to write the account of our recent journey, and last night I slept soundly for seven hours, for the first time in as many weeks.

I have come to understand that our group will, at some time or another, come across the York Factory Express making its way eastwards. I am resolved to write letters in time, so that they may be carried home to Britain.

Journal: Fort Assiniboine, 6 March 1851

54° 20' 3" N

We arrived at this place several days ago, after travelling for six days from Fort Edmonton. After the relative ease of the Saskatchewan valley, we faced a more difficult route climbing through a heavily wooded country, following a north-west course. Our progress slowed a little to about 10–15 miles each day, on account of the hills and also the snow, which here has been a very fine powder. I'm told a track has been cleared along this route and, during the summer months, travel between the two forts is possible in as little as two days. For us, the only sign of it has been the cleared way between the trees.

Unlike the lowlands, the increased exposure to the wind in this country affected us greatly. All of us have suffered frostnip, with ugly patches and scabs forming on any part unprotected. Some among us have black patches of dead skin on our noses and ears, and one has lost all feeling in the fingers of both his hands. For my part, the tip of my nose is red, but nothing more. I am relieved that my other extremities fare well.

The fort is built on the banks of the Athabasca River, which here is wide and sinuous. We will have fresh dogs before we leave, but for two days the wind has prevented us from doing so. It has been howling around the eaves of our modest shelter, and we are forced to wait here until the white fury subsides. Visibility in the blizzard is almost at zero, snow whipped up from old drifts melding with fresh precipitation.

Journal: Jasper House, 23 March 1851

58° 8' 49" N

There was much celebration when we reached this place on 21st March. Jasper House stands at an altitude of 3,500 feet in a broad valley. The principal structure is a simple wooden building with an overhanging roof and portico, situated near the river. Around it are various other small buildings, together with a few Indian shelters. Beyond are the most imposing mountains I have ever seen, more an enormous stone wall, with only a fringe of meagre *Coniferae* at their base. It is a lonesome place that only passing travellers frequent, yet compared to the climbing we must conquer ahead, I suspect I will soon wish I was still here among its meagre comforts.

To reach here from Fort Assiniboine, we made a gradual ascent for most of the distance, which was about 250 miles, and during the last two days we began a steeper climb through more mountainous terrain. All the way we followed the Athabasca River. Altogether, by my estimation, to reach this place from Cumberland House, where I joined the Winter Packet, we have travelled at least 1,100 miles on foot, or more likely nearer to 1,200 miles allowing for diversions, among them hunting for game or overcoming obstacles.

Had I not read before the exploits of men like Mr Douglas, I might never have thought it possible that any man could travel so great a distance in such a country as this. Now I find myself among those who have done so, I am not a little amazed at my own ability. I cannot help wonder if my employers have much notion, if any at all, of the hardships of crossing this great continent, even before I am able to execute my botanical duties by reaching Oregon Country. I can only pray that I reach the promised land with all my fingers in their place, and with my sight intact, otherwise I will be of little use to plant science, and a great disappointment to the investors.

Regular use by others has maintained an area of the river free of ice for fishing. We have enjoyed some excellent white fish. One is a little like the grayling I know from home, having a long dorsal fin and rainbow-coloured flanks. It is a beautiful fish.

I expect to remain here for some weeks, in the hope that we will meet the eastward Express, and exchange information and letters. We must not wait over-long before we cross the highest pass, or the great melt will be against us.

Journal: Jasper House, 1 April 1851

I had begun to write a letter to Prof Balfour, only to remember, with much shame, that I've made no direct communication with my dear family since leaving Britain. It was agreed that they would be kept informed of my progress by officers at the Garden, but I am remiss for not writing directly. I will write tomorrow and hopefully gain a clear conscience. I hope both letters will be collected when the eastbound York Express passes this way in a month or so.

I am undecided whether I will send my journals with the next consignment back to Britain. I like to read them during idle times, and they make a good companion. As my contract dictates, I copied my early entries in duplicate, but I fear this discipline has been quite lost to the wilderness.

Letter: John Jeffrey to his parents

Jasper House
Rocky Mountains
2nd April 1851

Mr and Mrs J. Jeffrey
Lochleven Road
Lochore
Fife

My dear Sir and beloved Mother,

I hope that news of my progress, in letters to Professor Balfour, has been relayed to you. There is so much to tell you otherwise; I would not know where to begin. Since leaving London I have sailed 2,600 miles across the ocean, and on this great continent, travelled 680 miles inland and upriver by boat through Rupert's Land, and a further 1,200 miles on foot through the snow of the British Territories to reach this place, on the east of the Rocky Mountains. Yet my outward journey is not over; I have next to cross the highest point before I descend to the west side of the mountains and head towards the Pacific Ocean. Only then, when I reach Oregon Country, will I be able to commence the real purpose of my expedition.

Besides my remaining enthusiasm for botany, I've derived much satisfaction from learning to sail and row, from travelling by dogs and with snowshoes, and most of all, in the ways of the Indian. They manage to live with little more than those items that can be fashioned from their animals and plants, although most have a liking for our tobacco and tea. I have yet to meet any who deserve the fearsome reputation so often held at home.

I am well in body, feeling both fit and strong. Mostly, the food is plentiful and wholesome, and only a few times have I been in need, and only then for a short while. I am often busy with my gun, and my skill in fetching game has made me popular with other men at every stage.

I hope this letter will reach the only ship of the Hudson's Bay Company to depart to Britain each year. It may be the same one that brought me here, leaving York Factory in September.

I am no longer the green man to whom you bade farewell in Edinburgh, and if it is God's wish that I see you before too long, you may need to hear my voice before you recognise me. Please remember me to any person who may know me.

Believe me to be most affectionately and truly,

Your loving son,

John

Letter: John Jeffrey to Professor Balfour †

Jasper House
Rocky Mountains
7th April 1851

To J. H. Balfour, M.D.
Regius Professor of Botany in the University of Edinburgh

Sir, — it is with much pleasure that I embrace this opportunity of writing to Britain; it being the first time that has occurred to me since my departure from York Factory. I have little doubt that long before this reaches you I will be considered by you all far out of my duty for not reporting my progress sooner. I am sorry to say that the means of doing so did not present itself to me in any shape before this date.

I left York Factory on 20th of August and got to Cumberland House on 6th of October. There I had to remain for the winter. The rivers and lakes were all getting covered with ice, putting travelling by water to an end, the only means that this part of the country affords. During my stay at Cumberland it was out of my power to forward the objects of the Expedition in any shape whatever. The collecting of insects was impractical, owing to the severity of climate. The birds, with the exception of a few species that are found at that place, are only summer visitors; they had taken their departure before my arrival. My opportunities for collecting en route were limited, as I had of course to keep with the Brigade, seldom having an opportunity of travelling by land. The country is so thickly covered with underwood, and so swampy, that I could seldom walk along the banks of the river.

The Brigade that proceeds to the west of the Rocky Mountains does not start from York Factory at the time I understood it did. From the information I received before I left Britain, I was made to understand that it left York Factory on the arrival of the ships from England, and proceeded on as far as the winter would allow them, starting again as soon as the rivers opened the navigation in Spring. On my inquiries after landing at York Factory, I found that such was not the case.

The only Brigades that start from York Factory on the arrival of the ships from England are sent down from the interior posts for their supplies, returning with it to their different districts. In company of one of those Brigades I started. The Brigade that proceeds to the west of the Rocky Mountains starts from Fort Vancouver on the Columbia River sometime in March, reaches York Factory about the end of June, starts again about the beginning of July and reaches Fort Vancouver, its starting place, sometime in the month of November. The only means besides this is what is called the Winter Packet. This packet starts from York Factory in the month of December and is carried by men on their backs from post to post till it reaches the Rocky Mountains. I have made this known to you, that you may understand how I was situated, so that you will be better able to judge whether the measures that I have adopted are in accordance with your views or not. In the first place, after weighing matters thoroughly, I considered, from what I have seen of the country to the east of the mountains, that a summer spent in it would be a summer lost; and if I remained for the Brigade that crosses the mountains, winter would meet me as soon as I reached those Mountains. Again, I found that it was impossible to proceed in company of only a few people, from several causes. We would, in the first place, have to pass through the extensive prairies along the Saskatchewan Rivers, inhabited by hostile tribes of Indians; and in the second, after getting to the Mountains, the rivers would be so much swollen that they would prove great barriers.

I made up my mind to start in company with the men that carried the Winter Packet, and if my strength would stand me, endeavour to continue on from coast to coast till I reached the Rocky Mountains. On 3th of January this packet reached Cumberland House. I had all my preparations made to be ready for a start as soon as it arrived. I was furnished with four dogs to drag my baggage that I found necessary to take along with me. What I could dispense with for the first summer I left at Cumberland, to be forwarded by the Columbia Brigade to Fort Vancouver.

I continued to trudge on from post to post, getting a fresh man and fresh dogs at every post that I came to en route. I generally remained at each station for a few days to refresh for another stage. The route lay along the Saskatchewan River to Edmonton House; after that we steered in the NW course through the woods, and fell on the Athabasca River at Fort Assiniboine. We travelled by the course of that river all the way to Jasper House, at which place we arrived on 21st of March. All this distance I walked on snowshoes, the snow being on average 2 feet deep. The distance from Cumberland to Jasper House is 1,200 miles. During this journey I slept with no other covering than that found under the friendly Pine, for the space of 47 nights, on several occasions the thermometer standing from 30° to 40° below zero. I found no bad effects from exposure. The only thing that happened to me was that once or twice I got slightly frost bit; that was nothing uncommon among us, and little cared for.

In the space of five or six days I expect to be able to start from this place, and get to the west flank of the Mountains before the thaw commences on the top of the Mountains. From that I shall be able to follow the route laid down in my instructions, and I am in hope of making a rich harvest. From what information I have collected from some of the Officers of the Hudson's Bay Company, I shall be able to pilot my own course to the Pacific, in a north-west direction. If I were once across this barrier that is before me, then God willing, in 10 days more I expect to be on the height of land; summer will then be at my feet, which will allow me to commence my labours at once. I have already reached the region of the *Pinus Douglasii*. In the proper season, seed could be collected here in any quantity of this noble pine.

I have collected since my arrival at this place a good many beetles, likewise some birds. Amongst the birds are fine specimens. I believe there is a fine grass not common in collections in Britain.

The small Collections that I have made since my arrival in the country will reach Britain by the return of the Hudson's Bay Company's ship; my Journals, up to this date, will likewise accompany the objects. The collections that I may make this summer will not reach England before the autumn of 1852; that is, if I don't find an opportunity of sending them via Panama at the close of the season.

Before then it is out of my power to forward anything worthy of distribution; I am sure that many will be longing for something to recompense their outlay. As soon as I am possessed of the objects I shall lose no chance of getting them forwarded, only avoiding the sending of anything perishable by Cape Horn or Cape of Good Hope.

My expenditure with the Hudson's Bay Company has not

yet exceeded £30. I took many things from York Factory, in the way of supplies of different kinds, for a whole year. When I made up my mind to start with the winter packet, I got all my surplus stock disposed of at Cumberland, at no loss. This, of course, is charged by the Hudson's Bay Company the same; but I have the money received for what I disposed of, which is available at any time. I intend making as full a collection of the *Coniferae* of America as may be in my power. Some of the common sort I will only preserve a few specimens, for such purpose as adding them to the riches, which I hope will soon be, contained in the Royal Botanic Garden Museum.

I will write by the first opportunity from the west side of the Mountains. I would not be surprised if that letter will reach you before this.

I have little more to add at this time. I hope to have a letter from you this summer. I will reach Fort Vancouver from the north, in all likelihood, this autumn; at all events, that will be a place where my letters will be safest to be addressed to me; there I will always find them.

I am, Sir,
Your humble servant,
John Jeffrey

Email: Arnold Arboretum, Boston, 20 October, present day

From: helen@arnoldarboretum.org

Hi Ben,

Good to have had that quick chat yesterday.

Like I said, still nothing formally agreed with RBGE about the visit, but I'm making good progress with the research. I'm in touch quite regularly with their librarian, who continues to be really helpful.

It's reassuring, from what I've read so far, that his journal entries sync with the archive material, which I've now sorted by date and catalogued (but not yet read all of).

I find the timescales mind-blowing. The expedition's organisers in Scotland were usually at least six months behind knowing what JJ was up to, sometimes more.

In terms of reading progress, I'm now in the spring of 1851. It's almost 10 months since he set out, and he's still not in the 'country' (i.e. Oregon Country) he was charged with exploring. Just the small feat of crossing the Rockies before he can start botanising! Also, it seems JJ was undecided whether he should yet submit his first journals, and then, in a rare letter to Balfour just one week later, he says he will include them alongside other items to be sent to Edinburgh. Curious.

H.

Journal: Jasper House, 18 April 1851

The Columbia Express arrived today from the other side of the Rocky Mountains. With them travelled Mr Robert Clouston, chief trader from Fort Victoria. It was a reassurance that he had been made aware of my expedition, and that he would be returning with me and acting as a guide as far as Fort Colville.

This means that I will part company with Caleb, who is to travel back to York Factory with the Saskatchewan Express. I cannot say we ever became familiar with one another, but I have much respect for the man, who is imperturbable. Notwithstanding the hardships nature prepared for us, or any weaknesses in human spirit that emerged, he led with a fierce confidence, and inspired us all that we were capable of the feat in which we ultimately succeeded.

Journal: Crossing Athabasca Pass, 26 April 1851

52° 7' 00" N

I write from the Boat Encampment on 2nd May. We left Jasper House on 26th April. Each of the following days, we were on our feet by 3 a.m. to take advantage of some hours of a crust on the snow. The route through Athabasca Pass was wild and daunting, surrounded on all sides by majestic peaks, everywhere thick with snow and ice. Being among these great peaks reminded me of Humboldt, and his ascent of Chimborazo.

Often I believed there was no route ahead, and on looking behind, was surprised we had passed through the land intact. The snow was always deep and our little group trudged on in snowshoes while the dogs seemed keen to run. I believe all of us held in our hearts an expectation, not so much of the culmination to come in successfully traversing the highest part of the Rocky Mountains – though that would be a cause for both celebration and relief – but more a longing for green, for spring, for the land of promise which lay beyond.

Before the pass itself, we made Athabasca Falls with the help of horses, following a well-prepared track. It was a wonderful sight of tangled and jagged walls of frozen water, which were already melting. Here we finally parted company with the Athabasca River, and the horses, to ascend south-west towards the pass.

We were blessed with fine weather for the high traverse. Our greatest elevation at Athabasca Pass itself was 5,750 feet, in fact, merely some 500 feet lower than Humboldt's climb to the peak of Chimborazo. It is testament to the scale of this range that the great peaks surrounding the pass tower above so much higher still. Nearby, at the Committee Punch Bowl – as tradition dictates – we celebrated with three cheers and a generous measure of rum.

To the west of this place is the dominant peak of Mount Brown, named after the illustrious botanist Robert Brown by no less than David Douglas himself when he passed here in 1827. To the south, its sister Mount Hooker looked on, also named by Mr Douglas. It was curious to think of Sir William Hooker in these circumstances, after our less than convivial meeting in London.

After the elation of conquering the pass came a long and tiring descent, one section in particular being so precipitous that a simple slip would have meant the end to any of our souls. We followed the Wood River – crossing its frozen waters many times – to where it meets the Columbia River. Only as we neared our destination did the snow and ice retreat to reveal some of the ground underneath. We used the gravel battures to our advantage, making rapid progress where otherwise the ground was terribly boggy.

The route of 120 miles took in total six days, all of us now enjoying the safety of this place they call the Boat Encampment, on account of this being the start of the navigable river, or perhaps because of the excellent birch all round which they use for building canoes.

I am, at last, in Oregon Country, or more correctly 'Territory' as they now call it.

Journal: Boat Encampment, 3 May 1851

Now, being below the tree line, we are able keep ourselves comfortably warm, although even in the tents that we've secured it remains a little cold at night.

Mr Clouston told me that we will rest here two more days. I have made some modest excursions along a great bend in the Columbia River, exploring the forests round the mouth of the Canoe River which flows from the north. I have been hunting for game, not trees, as our fitness requires it.

From here we will take to canoes, the water now running free of ice, to descend the Columbia River.

Specimen: No. 21, *Scilla* Sp., 13 May 1851 †

Columbia, near Colville.

Found on dry sand-banks. Height 2 feet. Flowers in umbrels.
Dark blue. (Not many seeds)

Journal: Fort Colville, 14 May 1851

48° 37' 42" N

My transit across this great continent is finally over; and so my work can begin in earnest. Despite the labours of reaching this place, I feel more energised than exhausted, and, after so long a wait, I am keen to start the work for which I am employed.

Fort Colville (where we arrived 12th May) is a thriving trading post and an assault on the senses for men at ease in silent company, and after so long in the wilderness. From Jasper House to reach this place was, in total, 350 miles.

I intend to spend one week or more here, refreshing provisions and exploring the local plant life, which is bursting forth now that spring has arrived with full vigour. I found a beautiful dark blue flowering species of *Scilla* yesterday; I hope the few seeds I could find will be well received at home.

I have been introduced to the chief trader at this Fort, Mr Alexander Caulfield Anderson, who has generously offered to guide me most of the way to Fort Victoria. He is the grandson of a Scottish botanist himself, which is quite the coincidence. His young son James has decided, with little else to do beyond his studies and light duties, that I am a source of entertainment. He has attached himself to me, so much so that I must be firm with him even to gain a little personal privacy for the most basic of functions.

Mr Clouston will be leaving tomorrow to return, via Walla Walla, to Fort Victoria. Our onward party will be myself and Mr Anderson, together with Wahiya, who evidently seems to enjoy my company. He has no business away from the main HBC route, other than his curiosity for adventure, and not a little interest in the ocean. It has been the topic of much conversation between us, being a creation he has determined to see with his own eyes.

Specimen: No. 27, *Penstemon* Sp., 15 May 1851 †

Columbia, near Colville.

Found growing on dry rocky places. Flowers purple, perennial. 1 foot high.

Journal: Fort Colville, 18 May 1851

Accompanied by 10-year-old James, I explored the banks of the little Colville River which meanders along a wide valley in a southward direction. There was little of botanical interest. I collected a few beetle specimens from under the decomposing stem of a fallen giant fir (too rotten to identify). I have seen many prints of bears and their scratching posts, but was quite taken aback to find, in the centre of one fresh and giant paw print, the tiniest of shrews with fur in three shades of grey. It seemed quite unharmed in every way, as though it had laid down to rest in this bear's depression and never woken. The thought occurred to me that this would be the start of a great legend, if I were to mention it to Wahiya.

At the edge of the woods I shot a handsome woodpecker. Possessing prominent barring on its back and flanks, it caught my eye; it's the first of its kind I've seen, having a dashing yellow crown. I was surprised further to notice, while I prepared it for my collection, that it had three rather than the usual four toes on each foot.

Young James was evidently impressed with my mark, this being quite a small bird, and at dinner regaled every person with the tale, which as the evening lengthened, he made sound more and more extraordinary.

Specimen: No. 32, *Lewisia rediviva*, 16 June 1851 †

Columbia

This pretty little plant is only found in dry arid places on pure sand. The Indians eat its roots and consider it to be one of the Great Spirit's greatest gifts to them. The Indian name is Spetlum. *The roots have an agreeable flavour when boiled, rather bitter. I have no doubt it will prove to be an excellent tonic. Flowers, rose, large; leaves about an inch long, narrow and awl-shaped. (Not many seeds).*

Journal: Okanogan and Similkameen Rivers, 9 July 1851

48° 56' 4" N

We departed Fort Colville on 28th May, then explored the Columbia River valley by following its course downstream until it reached the Okanogan. From there we followed its stream until it met the Similkameen.

This hilly country is proving fruitful for botanising. Mr Anderson and Wahiya have struck up a cordial relationship and seem content to converse about all matters while I complete my excursions. Thanks to both men, I have been afforded each evening the luxury of a prepared encampment and fresh food, leaving me the time to explore and record with little regard for my personal needs.

I have amassed well over 100 botanical samples, including the seeds of many herbaceous plants.

Journal: Similkameen and Tulameen, 10 July 1851

49° 27' 51" N

We continued to follow the Similkameen upstream until its junction with the Tulameen River. We made camp shortly after.

Before sunset, while dangling my feet to cool them near a point, I noticed a golden glimmer from the bed of the river. Curiosity demanded a better look and, on wading in and scooping it up, I was dumbfounded to find in my hand a single smooth gold nugget. Shaped a little in the fashion of a kidney bean, it was wider than my finger and surprisingly heavy. I knew at once what it was, even though I have never held gold in this form before.

It was the only nugget I could see, yet surely where there was one, there must be more – perhaps smaller flakes among the silt, or maybe even larger nuggets among the gravel.

Making sure I had not been observed, I placed it quietly in my purse. Mention of this will, I fear, not bode well for this expedition. I have recorded the latitude of the place, and described the location in some detail in a separate note that I will keep with the gold. I must think more what to do with it.

Journal: Campement des Femmes, 12 July 1851

49° 32' 46" N

This place is so named after the Tulameen women, who remain here when the menfolk leave to hunt or go warring. It's also a regular encampment for the HBC Express, whose tents and huts fill the flats near Otter Lake. Steep-sided hills, studded with pines, crowd the meandering river.

Mr Anderson told me he was charged, three years ago, with finding a new route for the HBC when the US border was moved, following the signing of the Treaty for the Territory of Oregon. He pioneered a route following the

Tulameen River, whose tortuous route we have followed recently. We will soon move on upstream towards its source: a small round lake that he called the 'Punch Bowl'.

Wahiya stayed behind while I made two local excursions from this place, seeming to have found some fruitful company among the Indians. I think perhaps it may be a woman, but he is very coy, keeping his actions and thoughts to himself. I may even have seen him blush when I enquired as to his business.

Specimen: No. 180, *Claytonia*, 19 July 1851 †

Campement des Femmes. Lat. 49° 51'.

Elevation 6,000 feet; perennial; a fine alpine species; growing to the height of 9 or 10 inches; flowers pink; chasms of granite rocks.

Specimen: No. 183, *Penstemon*, 19 July 1851 †

Near Campement des Femmes. Lat. 49°50'.

Growing out of the chasms of the rocks; elevation 6,000 feet. Perennial.

Specimen: No. 184, *Penstemon*, 19 July 1851 †

Campement des Femmes.

Near the base of the mountain. Perennial. Along the bank of a small stream on clay soil.

Specimen: No. 188, *Penstemon*. 20 July 1851 †

Summit of Manson's Mountain, east of Francis Rover. Few seeds.

Journal: Fort Hope, 22 July 1851

49° 23' 09" N

After reaching the source of the Tulameen River, Wahiya and I parted company with Mr Anderson, who proceeded straight on towards Fort Langley. It was a heartfelt goodbye, for he is a good-natured man.

We followed a rugged trail, leaving the main route to ascend Mount Manson. We were rewarded with a spectacular view over the route by which we had come, and looking the opposite way, eastwards towards where the Pacific Ocean must surely lie. I could sense its presence, even though it lay beyond a haze. The peak itself was quite barren, made of great columns of granite.

During our descent to Fort Hope we passed through steep Alpine meadows, rich with an abundance of flowering plants, especially where sheltered by belts of *Coniferae*. Evidently, the moisture-laden westerlies benefit plant growth, even at this altitude. Time and light were both against us, but I collected several promising herbaceous specimens; among these, a most attractive *Penstemon* which formed mats among the rocks and crevices. Its tubular flowers are the colour of lavender and much larger than may be supposed, given the dwarf nature of the plant itself.

The fort is a simple collection of buildings, including a small store, surrounded on one side by the Fraser River, and on the other a wooden palisade. The mountains rise so steeply behind, they appear like a wall. This is the place where all Brigades heading to the interior switch from boats to horses. Tomorrow, we hope to take advantage of their empty York boats to enjoy rapid passage downstream to Fort Langley, and then to the ocean itself.

Journal: Fort Langley, 24 July 1851

49° 10' 33" N

We descended the Fraser River, covering the final 60 miles to Fort Langley in just two days. Apart for a few miles of intermittent gentle rapids, formed by large gravel banks, we passed through a final mountain gateway to enjoy a languid passage; some of the most relaxing hours I've experienced for longer than I care to remember. Our final approach to Fort Langley was on tidal water, this being the first since the other side of the continent, 2,500 miles distant (by my estimate).

The fort has a large collection of buildings, surrounded by a considerable wooden palisade, leaning outwards as if trouble is expected at any moment. There are more people here than I have seen in one place since London. Furs arrive daily downriver, carried by Indians and other traders, which the HBC organises ready for despatch to Britain. There is little to keep me here and I intend to take the first available ship downriver for the last 40 miles, and thence to Vancouver Island and Fort Victoria. Mr Anderson – with whom we've been reunited – already seems burdened by administrative duties. Meanwhile, Wahiya and I explored the docks and there we came across a street vendor frying Island oysters. My friend experienced his first taste of the sea – his face was a picture I shall never forget.

Journal: Fort Victoria, 27 July 1851

48° 26' 11" N

The passage here was uneventful, except for Wahiya's joyous whoop – which attracted much attention – at the moment he glimpsed the vastness of the ocean. It was visible beyond the strait for only a short while as we tacked to and fro before entering the harbour.

Thanks to Mr Anderson, I have been afforded

comfortable accommodation in the HBC quarters for unmarried men. Wahiya has found his own place a short distance away.

Last evening I joined the governor of Vancouver Island, Mr James Douglas (another Douglas!), for dinner. He apparently will regularly invite all the HBC officers to his house. He is also the chief factor for the HBC; virtually every person here is connected with the HBC in diverse ways, from clerks to sailors to Métis guides. I heard that the previous governor discovered that the HBC rule over this place was so absolute that he retired with high stress; poor fellow.

They have formed a new military troop, as there seems to be a great nervousness about possible violence from the Indians, and it no doubt also maintains the peace among the colonists. The troop are not British, but volunteers – mostly of Métis descent – and known as 'Victoria Voltigeurs'. They walk about boldly in a uniform of red and blue, wearing a Canadian coat or capote, with a red woollen sash over one shoulder. Two were bold enough to ask my business one evening, when I was following the fortifications in the company of Wahiya.

Many people here – from HBC men, to pioneers and miners, to natives – lapse into a pidgin jargon which they call 'Lelang', which I suppose has come from the native Chinook, melded with French and English. I have learned that *stick* means a tree, and a *whim stick* a fallen tree, while some words need little learning, like 'ship'!

During dinner (*muck-a-muck!*) I took the opportunity, by way of a short speech, to thank my companion Mr Anderson for his good company and wise counsel, and to recognise the support of the HBC overall towards my expedition. There was interest in my work, yet most talk was of California and the gold rush which continues unabated. Even more sensational was news that the City of San Francisco has suffered from more than one great fire, with thousands of buildings destroyed (and no doubt as many people), while several earthquakes have also been felt there. One man, freshly arrived, described it as a lawless violent place, thronging with off-duty prospectors, and with frequent public hangings.

Among the politics discussed, there was mention of 'manifest destiny'. As it was explained to me, this means the great mission of conquering the West, and the sense of patriotic duty for all new American people to be productive. I suppose that I too am playing a small part in this irresistible destiny.

I have received advice as to what parts of the island may be fruitful for me to explore. Apparently, the interior is quite impenetrable, due to the thickness of the scrub.

Journal: Fort Victoria, 28 July 1851

There was hushed talk during dinner this evening of a gold rush that had started on the Queen Charlotte Islands in March of this year. It began when an Indian from that place (about 140 miles north of this island) arrived in Fort Victoria, and traded a 27-ounce nugget for 1,500 HBC blankets.

The HBC soon afterwards despatched a ship to visit the south island, where they were successful in discovering a rich vein and started to blast it, but found the Indians (known as the Haida) were quickly among them to take their own share. After much effort, the ship set sail with more than $1,500 dollars' worth of gold on board, only to be wrecked on the approach to the straits that lead to the fort here. All the hard-earned gold was lost.

Mr Douglas was most obviously still frustrated by the whole affair, and discussed with his officers how the territory could be protected from exploitation by the Americans, notwithstanding the actions of the Haida.

I thought again of my own discovery, and wondered about its value. I trust no one in considering its worth. Gold rumours fly faster than any other news, and seem to bring mostly violence, misery, or both.

Journal: Mullachard, 29 July 1851

In the company of the chief surveyor, Captain Walter Colquhoun Grant, I rode some 20 miles west of Fort Victoria, where I am now a guest at his home. He has named it 'Mullachard', to remember his Strathspey roots. He has introduced Scottish broom to a garden (of sorts) which is in bright yellow flower. I feel quite at home.

I find him an extraordinary fellow. His father was the Duke of Wellington's chief intelligence officer at Waterloo, and he has inherited the classic bearing of a military man. Standing some inches taller than 6 feet, he confessed his fondness for cricket. He proudly showed me his bat and stumps, but I fear there is nowhere in the wilderness which surrounds his home where he could ever hope to play, and if he ever did, he would need a plentiful supply of balls – he would have no hope of recovering them from the scrub.

There seems no passage beyond here, the bush being very thick on all sides. Along the route to reach this place were some damp clearings which harboured a rich plant life.

Specimen: No. 380, *Malvaceae* Sp., 29 July 1851 †

Mullachard, Vancouver's Island. Found in moist prairies; flowers purple; plant 18 inches high.

Journal: Two gentlemen, 2 August 1851

Returning to Fort Victoria, I was invited to dinner this evening by Mr John Ballenden, who is a most congenial gentleman. He serves as chief factor at Fort Vancouver, and was very keen that I call upon his hospitality when my expedition turns to the south. He has only recently returned from England, taking furlough to recover, following an illness. We have agreed to dine together again tomorrow, and I am anxious to hear more news from home.

Yesterday, I was introduced to Cornish plant collector Mr William Lobb. He is collecting seeds on behalf of Mr James Veitch, the nurseryman of Exeter, who I know to be also a subscriber to my expedition. It is curious that Mr Veitch is investing in more than one venture, although this surely demonstrates the potential value of his reward.

Mr Lobb shared some of his considerable collecting experiences with me, having travelled extensively in the South Americas, and being perhaps twice my age. He was somewhat guarded concerning details of his collections along the west coast of California. He described seeing some very large *Coniferae*; and shared a rumour of giant trees having stems so huge that, when felled, the stump would comfortably provide the platform for a large house, and the timbers the frames for several more. He did not say where he thought these trees were, and it seems a little fanciful to my mind.

It is fortunate we have met one another, as I can ensure my excursions focus on where he has not yet explored.

Journal: Fort Rupert, 14 August 1851

50° 41' 24" N

Most of this island has remained out of reach due to its quite impenetrable bush. My repeated attempts to penetrate it have met with rare success, and more usually many cuts and bruises. Talking with Mr Ballenden, he suggested I should ask the HBC for passage to Fort Rupert at the north of the island, where I might find conditions more favourable.

This is therefore how I find myself here, on the northern tip of the island. I sailed on the steamship *Beaver* on a short passage, following its western shoreline. It provided an excellent view of the bush from afar, and even though it was often shrouded in mists, I could observe how it formed a formidable green skirt around the entire island, crowned by a towering canopy of *Coniferae*. No doubt inland much of it is virgin territory and ripe for plunder, if only it could be reached.

Near to shore we watched a large number of whales breaking the surface, which our captain called grampus. They were very sleek, being mostly black, and possessing a long scythe-like dorsal fin. Their bellies and large eye patches were a bright white. Apparently this species hunts seals and even larger ocean-going whales, working together in packs. I admit I found these creatures to be awesome, but they were not so large as those I saw near the end of my Atlantic passage. Wahiya, however, trembled visibly; I believe in part from excitement as to the size of the creatures, and no doubt otherwise from fear. He remained silent for a long time afterwards, leaning on the railing to gaze over the vastness of the ocean.

Shortly after, as we navigated towards the harbour, a freak wave caught us side-on. Wahiya found himself flung sideways and landed awkwardly, straight away discovering that a large fishhook had become embedded in the flesh of his upper arm. Fearful of the damage we might cause by trying to remove its barb, we bandaged it tightly to stem the flow of blood. Mercifully, there is a very competent surgeon of German descent, Dr Helmeken, who serves this small community. He removed the hook and stitched him up with consummate skill. I learned later that the children call him 'Dr Heal-my-skin'!

There are many miners based at the fort, many of them Scottish lads, charged with extracting coal for the HBC's steamships from what, by all accounts, is a meagre seam. I wouldn't say this seems a happy place, nor does it offer much comfort.

Journal: Fort Rupert, 16 August 1851

Wahiya's arm remains swollen and raging, though he is a little better in himself.

I admit that I have not ranged far without him as a companion, and there seems little enthusiasm from any other here to accompany me into the interior. I heard a story that a tribe of the local Indians, known as the Ku-Koltz, had resolved a local conflict by mounting the heads of 16 rivals on poles arranged along the shoreline. Unfortunately, this was the first sight that greeted some of these settlers when arriving here, and they remain ill at ease with the Indians.

I had some success with my gun. I bagged three brace of blue grouse where the bush came near the fort, and on the shoreline I took a very fine mature bald eagle from which I stripped its finer feathers.

After mentioning the grampus to some company men at dinner, there was talk of the whaler *Ann Alexander*, which only this summer was rammed by a larger species while it was hunting it in the South Pacific. By all accounts, the whale turned to ram the ship after receiving many harpoons from its boats. The papers reported that all men were saved by another ship two days later, but I cannot say that I have no sympathy for the whale, which was so cruelly provoked.

I have decided to return, empty-handed, to Fort Victoria.

Journal: Autumn excursion, 24 August 1851

I am pleased to note that Wahiya is fully recovered. This afternoon, I met a local Métis man and made a very good trade for the eagle feathers, receiving in return a pouch of placer gold weighing 1/100th ounce.

Feeling well settled at Fort Victoria, I have resolved to undertake an autumn excursion into the interior of the mainland, aiming to reach a high latitude to take advantage of the possibility of an abundance of ripe seed from the

Coniferae. This will be the last opportunity for collecting this year, and it will likely please the Association.

Following several conversations with Mr Anderson, who has been most generous with his advice, I have elected to follow a little-tested route into the interior, with the intention of reaching the plateau above the famed Fraser Canyon, where he tells me there are large swathes of unexplored forest.

The route which he has described in detail will take us northwards, following the Squamish River, and then broadly north-east between high glaciated mountains, reaching two long ribbon lakes before reaching the Fraser. He has drawn the route for me by hand, creating a most impressive map which we will have to rely on, there being likely no colonials in this region to help us.

We depart tomorrow.

Journal: Chilcotin, 16 September 1851

51° 49' 48" N

There has been little opportunity to note progress. In any case, I carry in my possession only this single almost-complete journal, and no more, so I must ration my writing. Our route here has been arduous, the terrain being very rugged. Leaving the Fraser River, we travelled north, then westwards along a smaller tributary, climbing all the distance. This is the furthest north I have travelled since crossing the Rocky Mountains. Many of the peaks here are 8,000 feet in altitude or more.

The Indians here call themselves the Chilcotin, and although we have been unable to understand each other's words, Wahiya has found the means to make our intentions clear and we have been made quite welcome. They are camped along the banks of the river in large numbers, here for the run of salmon.

Specimen: No. 206, *Rhododendron* Sp., 20 September 1851 †

Growing on mountains east of the Fraser River, Lat. 50°, elevation 6,000 feet. Growing on vegetable soil. A deciduous shrub, growing 3 feet high. Flowers white. (Few seeds.)

Specimen: No. 207, *Rhododendron* Sp., 20 September 1851 †

Found growing in the same locality with No. 206 but also at a greater elevation. This one is found near the snow line, that is, 8,000 feet above the sea in Lat. 50°.

Specimen: No. 393, *Picea* Sp., 22 September 1851 †

Found on the banks of the Fraser River, from the falls all the way down to the ocean. This tree resembles the Picea pectinata *of Europe. The only points in which it differs from that tree is in the smallness of its cones and its larger leaves. Found growing on the alluvial banks of the river near Fort Langley, 280 feet high, and 5 feet diameter, 50 feet without branches.*

Specimen: No. 398, *Pinus* Sp., 23 September 1851 †

Found on the summit of a mountain near Fort Hope, Fraser River. I could only find a few specimens of this tree on which there were cones, and on those few, Corvus Columbianus *had deprived them of nearly all their seeds. Leaves in fives, short and rigid, cones small nearly round, bark smooth, tree 30 feet high, 8 foot diameter, growing on granite decayed. Lat. 50°, elevation 7,000 feet.*

Specimen: No. 409, *Picea* Sp. 27 September 1851 †

Mountains east of Fraser River. Lat. 50°.

Found on the sloping sides of the mountains, growing on gravelly soil, at an elevation of 4,000 feet; leaves very small, dark green above, silvery beneath; detached cones, erect, ovate, oblong, 5 inches long, found only on the top of trees; branches horizontal, short and bushy; tree large 250 feet high, 5 feet diameter, 60 feet without branches; bark smooth and covered on the young trees with large globules filled with balsam; bark red; timber white and soft. This tree is seen from a great distance towering its head above all her sisters of the forest.

Minutes: Oregon Botanical Association, 29 September 1851 †

Edinburgh

Present:
David Smith
George Patton
W. Evans

Mr Smith in the Chair.

Present also Mr Veitch of Exeter, a Subscriber

Mr Smith stated that in consequence of the unavoidable absence of the Secretary he had to submit to the meeting a letter from Mr Jeffrey the Collector dated from Jasper House, Rocky Mountains, April 1851.

The letter was read and the meeting expressed themselves highly pleased with the zeal and energy Mr Jeffrey appears to have displayed in carrying out the objects of the Association, and requested Mr Smith as Chairman of the present meeting to communicate their sentiments to Mr Jeffrey.

As this was the first letter received from the Collector since he left York Factory, the meeting considered that it would be proper that its contents should be communicated generally to the Subscribers, and they therefore decided that the same should be printed and circulated.

Journal: Fort Hope, 1 October 1851

49° 38' 00" N

The Fraser Canyon is a fearful place, and without doubt, beyond any feasible passage by canoe or boat of any design I have ever seen. We followed it broadly southwards by traversing the rugged hills along its eastern flank, now and then drawing close to its hellish rapids, but never attempting to cross its stream. The roar of its waters was beyond any noise I have experienced. We will rest here one night and resupply.

Specimen: No. 209, *Gentiana*, 2 October 1851 †

Found on the margin of a small stream, at the base of Mount Baker, growing on sandy soil. Perennial.

Journal: Mount Baker, 16 October 1851

48° 46' 11" N

Leaving Fort Hope, we headed south to climb towards Mount Baker and its foothills. This is a most imposing mountain, being always visible from Vancouver Island. The counter views from near its peak, to the straits and the island beyond, were tremendous.

It has been a fruitful excursion in these hills, not least for the discovery of a very beautiful conifer whose pendulous branches sweep most gracefully to the ground. The tree is notable in having its needles arranged radially, and for its attractive narrow cones which mature to a dark purple-grey. The cones possess a wonderful resinous aroma – I have taken to carrying one in my coat pocket, where it has had a delectable effect on my general fragrance. It often grows in clumps around the alpine meadows, forming altogether a most agreeable vision, although I have also found it on the most exposed of ridges. I propose to name it after George Patton, the founder of the Oregon Botanical Association.

We are camped in a sheltered meadow among the flowers. From here we will descend westwards towards Fort Victoria. The first snows have already settled; I do not intend to stay in the back country and endure the same conditions as the last winter.

Specimen: No. 430, *Abies* Sp., 16 October 1851 †

Found on the Mount Baker range of mountains. This species makes its appearance at the point where Abies Canadensis *disappears, that is, at an elevation of about 5,000 feet above the sea; from that point to the margin of perpetual snow it is found. Along the lower part of its range it is a noble-looking tree, rising to the heights of 150 feet, 13 1/2 feet in circumference. As it ascends the mountains it gets gradually smaller till at last it dwindles into a shrub of not more than 4 feet high. Leaves solitary dark green above, silvery beneath, flat and rounded at their points, thickly placed round the branches, cones upwards of an inch long, produced at the points of the branches; branches pendulous; bark rough, of a greyish colour; timber hard and very fine in the grain, of a red colour. Soil on which this tree was growing most luxuriantly was red loam, very strong and moist. If this tree proves undescribed I hope it will be known under the name of* Abies Pattonii.

Journal: A heartfelt farewell, 18 October 1851

It is with a heavy heart that I mention that Wahiya and I parted ways today. Evidently now satisfied by his sight of the ocean and our travels together, he quickly made up his mind to join a band of men heading east, who we had come upon in the hills above Puget Sound. He seemed little perturbed by our farewell, but we did fondly embrace for a long moment. I passed him a small purse containing the placer gold that I had intended to give him when we reached Fort Victoria. He did not open it when we were together, but I think it will please him.

I admit that a little later, I shed a tear, on account of it being most improbable that I will see him again in my lifetime. He has been a very fine companion and we survived so many great challenges together across this wild continent – he is certainly well named. Our origins could not have contrasted to a greater degree, yet as the great Lavoisier laid down, we are neither created nor destroyed, but are of the same matter. Brothers in arms – brothers in nature.

Journal: San Juan Islands, 30 October 1851

On first returning to Fort Victoria, I found myself restless after a few days, and resolved to explore the San Juan Islands, which lie in the main strait within sight of the town. There is some tension between Britain and America over the territory, its ownership remaining unclear in the 1846 Treaty. During my short passage I spotted warships from both parties patrolling its narrow waters.

Nature on the islands is thriving with so few resident people, although the HBC fur trade has made its mark. There are beaver dams everywhere, but most appear uncared for and I saw very few of the animals. Yet, I have never seen so many great eagles in one place. The trees are magnificent here, especially the *Pinus Douglasii* which are very large (and make popular perches for the eagles). I made bountiful collections of seed from this and other *Coniferae*, to the extent that my day sack was overflowing, as were my pockets, before each day was out.

I visited three of the islands, camping overnight for four nights, yet there are many more of them I could yet explore. Being without a companion, I found plenty of time to reflect on my expedition overall, and to think again of home.

Now back in Fort Victoria again, my thoughts have turned towards next year and where I must focus my explorations. Mr Ballenden has been of much assistance in this regard. I have often enjoyed his company, and he has many stories to share. In 1836, he was at Fort Garry in the Red River District (where my *Prince of Wales* cabin-mate was headed), when he fell in love with a woman whom he later took for his wife; Sarah was an 18-year-old Métis, and daughter of the fort's chief factor Mr McLeod. She apparently nursed him back to health after he suffered a stroke four years ago, while he was travelling west on business. Before that time, one side of his body had been utterly paralysed. Sarah has been left behind while he is on business here, and he seems to miss her with a passion.

Minutes: Oregon Botanical Association, 6 November 1851 †

Botanic Gardens, Edinburgh

Present:
Professor Balfour in the Chair
Messrs Isaac Anderson, James McNab, W. Evans, Andrew Murray – Secretary

The Secretary stated that the meeting was called to be present at the opening of a Box which had been received from Mr Jeffrey.

The Meeting then proceeded to open the Box, when its contents were found to be as following:

Eight clusters of the cones of *Pinus Banksiana* (number being 105 cones) from the Hill River, taken 29 August 1850. These were chiefly Herbaceous specimens, having been pulled in a green state.

Five clusters of the cones of *Abies Nigra* (numbering 60 cones) from a tree 7 feet high on the banks of the Hay's River, 10 miles above York Factory, taken 20 August 1850. Cones immature.

Ten clusters of cones of the *Abies Nigra* (numbering 33 cones) from a tree 40 feet high and 6 inches in diameter, on the banks of the Saskatchewan River, taken on 30 September 1850.

Five clusters of cones of *Abies Rubra* (numbering 54 cones) from a tree 50 feet high, 9 inches in diameter, taken at Oxford House on 19 September 1850. Appear ripe.

Three clusters of cones of *Abies Alba* (numbering 22

cones) from a tree 100 feet high and 18 inches in diameter, taken at Oxford House on 19 September 1850. Appear ripe.

Nine clusters of cones of *Larix Pendula* (about 300 small cones about the size of a pea) from a tree 18 feet high, and branches very pendulous, taken on the banks of the River Saskatchewan near the Grand Rapids, 1 October 1850. Seem ripe.

The following Birds were found: Magpie from Cumberland House, Long-tailed grouse, Pine Bullfinch, A woodpecker. Also one small bottle of beetles, and one small wooden pill box of the same.

The Committee, considering that the seeds are so few in number and of such common kinds, as well as that many of the cones seem to have been pulled in a green state and consequently are unfit for the purpose of sowing, thought it advisable that no distribution of seeds should be made at present; but that they should be replaced in the box, and put aside in the meantime to await the further orders of the Committee. The Box was accordingly nailed up, and sealed.

Journal: A quiet revelation, 12 November 1851

Mr Ballenden and I have spent much time together during this dark and sodden month. Yesterday, he confided a sensational personal story to me. He is among the most genuine of men; generous, good-humoured, and soft-spoken. This made his story all the more distressing.

I have been largely blind to the niceties of society here, especially concerning females. Before 1830, he told me, white women were barred from accompanying HBC men; therefore any marriage between these men and Indian or half-bloods elevated the social station of these local women. By his account, such arrangements were perfectly satisfactory, both among the HBC and natives. Yet, the arrival of women from Britain and the Continent – who brought with them a certain expectation of treatment as a fairer sex and a natural air of superiority over the Indians – upset this easy affiliation. Thus, if an Indian female has an apparent status higher than a white female, gained via a marriage, for example, this can cause many difficulties, not least vicious backbiting and slander.

And so it seems that Mr Ballenden's Métis wife became affected by such circumstances, and to a loathsome degree. He told me he was away on business two years ago when poor Sarah – who he says is a rare beauty – had to spurn the advances of a young dandy army captain (whom I shall not name, though I know who he is). In some way, the frustrations of this man merged with a simmering discontent among some white women, who felt put out by the higher status of the chief factor's Métis wife, and were perhaps not without a little envy. Mr Ballenden arrived back at his post at Red River to find it split in two by speculation and scandal. Another captain, by the name of Foss, brought a lawsuit against this louse, wishing to protect the good name of Mrs Ballenden. The court took the side of Mrs Ballenden, and heavy damages were awarded, yet the position of the Ballendens at Red River became untenable. The community remained so strongly divided that Mr Ballenden says he suffered terribly from stress. He went on furlough in the autumn of that year with the sure knowledge he could never return to his post there.

Hence he has been posted as chief factor to Fort Vancouver, which is where he will depart for tomorrow. He has been without his wife all this time and knows little about how she truly fares at Red River, other than what she has chosen to share with him in a few letters.

Letter: HBC secretary to Andrew Murray †

Hudson's Bay House
London
17th November 1851

Andrew Murray, Esq.,
7 Nelson Street,
Edinburgh

Sir,

I have to acknowledge receipt of your letter of the 8th inst. and to acquaint you in reply that there was no journal sent in the box sent home by Mr Jeffrey.

    I am, Sir,
    Your obedient servant,
    A. Barclay,
    Secretary,
    Hudson's Bay Company

Journal: A small celebration, 14 November 1851

A small celebratory party was held this evening to mark the occasion of my 25th birthday. Mr Ballenden was a marvellous master of ceremonies, and not a little good wine was shared among us.

Journal: Fort Victoria, 31 December 1851

There has been little of consequence to record as I overwinter here. Mr Ballenden has left for San Francisco, accompanied by a Mr Ogden (whom I did not meet), travelling by steam ship. I found myself suffering from boredom to such an extent that I offered my services as part-time clerk to an HBC officer. This has kept me busy, whilst the modest wage has meant I can enjoy the evenings with less financial constraint.

All work has now stopped for three days, with many of those preceding being also taken up in preparations for the holiday. A great number of animals have been slain for feasting, stacks of grog barrels brought close by, and extra firewood prepared, so no person should have to work during the two-day festivities. I am told the third day is allowed for every person to recover from the revelry, before work begins as usual the next day. Spirits are lifted everywhere.

The weather has often been very cruel, and it is not uncommon for ships to find the harbour quite impossible to leave. The main yard at the fort is awash with mud; those familiar with the conditions from previous winters seem well prepared, routinely wearing their sea boots.

Last month I despatched Box No. 3 to Edinburgh, containing specimens collected throughout most of this year. It has been sent via San Francisco and thence will proceed round the Horn to London. It also contains a surprise artefact for the subscribers.

Shortly before sending the box, I traded 12 HBC blankets with a Haida Indian in exchange for a small grain of gold, or *pil chik-a-min* as he called it, I assume in Lelang. I believe he would have brought it from the southernmost tip of the Queen Charlotte Islands. Evidently, it was not the first time such a trade had been managed by this man, and he drove a hard bargain (*húy-húy*). I have quite often contemplated the irony of the discovery of this precious metal being coincidental with my own discoveries of living green 'gold'. These thoughts are not without a little mischief, but I think the subscribers will surely be reconsidering their green investment when news of the discoveries of gold – in the very same regions that I explore – reach their ears.

As for my own gold nugget from the Similkameen, I recently used the scales in the HBC stores when I found myself briefly alone. They were not the type designed for fine measuring, but I now have the knowledge that it weighs somewhat over 1/2 ounce. If I were a smart bargainer, I might expect ten dollars from trading it at a store, but I am told such places excel at extortion. The true value lies not in this single nugget, but in the others that must reside at the same origin. I find myself sometimes drawn to it, for it's a beautiful thing to look upon. It is shaped not unlike the continent of North America, but with none of its cragginess, smoothed instead to a golden molten pebble by the boiling action of the River Similkameen.

Prof Balfour and the other gentlemen will already be disappointed that my journals have not been sent, either with Boxes No. 1 or No. 2. I am even more sure that I cannot part with them, although had I made duplicate copies as instructed, it might have been possible. Yet, I have fallen into the habit of recording sentiments of a personal nature, and I would have to make two copies of a different essence to each other; one to share, one to keep. This is far too onerous while I have so many other duties to fulfil, and so many obstacles to contend with. In this regard, and only this regard, have I failed my employers. I consider that my letters, and the records I attach to the botanical specimens, should be quite adequate for the interests of the Association. Beyond this, I am resolved to write letters more frequently next year, in the hope that this will temper any frustrations at my performance. When I finally return home, I will be able to use my journals as the basis for a very full account, and at my own leisure.

Email: Arnold Arboretum, Boston, 11 November, present day

From: helen@arnoldarboretum.org

Hi Ben,

It seems that JJ was not as dutiful as we supposed. He deliberately withheld his journals from his employers.

In that letter I mentioned, written April 1851, he as good as promises to send them home with his next samples. Yet there's a letter I found from RBGE to the HBC in November that year, asking to check whether there were any in the box that had been received with plant samples. They were definitely getting a little pissed back in Edinburgh.

Then there's a dynamite admission in a journal entry I've just read, written at the end of 1851. He not only admits he's reluctant to part with them, but that he isn't copying them in duplicate either! He says it's 'too onerous'!

As you suggested, I've followed up with the field manager at RBGE re the visit, who has had a chat with the Regius Keeper. It sounds as though they are keen to host a visit. Apparently, they should be able to help with some free accommodation, too. Are you happy that I take the journals with me?

H.

P.S. I loved that purple tree tie you were wearing yesterday! I wanted to catch up with you after the talk, but you looked busy.

Email: Arnold Arboretum, Boston, 14 November,
present day

From: ben@arnoldarboretum.org

Dear Helen,

You're right, that really is dynamite!

It sounds like you're getting to grips with reading his hand now. It will be interesting to see if he mentions sharing his journals again, won't it?

Great news re your visit to RBGE – have you told anyone there about him deliberately withholding the journals? Talking of which, no, I don't think you should take them; I think they're way too valuable. I'll speak to our archivist about getting them scanned ASAP. When done, we can share them, but maybe not until you've finished working through them first ;-). Perhaps we could get some smart copies made up for them?

They're nice people, and they looked after me real well when I was there last August. Just to whet your appetite, I stayed in a long terrace of elegant grey stone houses near the gardens. They took me out to some amazing places in the Highlands, and to see a couple of great shows in a city festival called the 'Fringe'. Make sure you ask to try their haggis!

Best,

Ben

P.S. Yes, it's a nice tie; a gift from a former intern!

GERMINATION

1852

DEVELOPING FROM A SEED

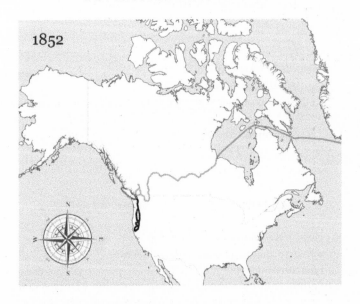

1852

Journal: Fort Rupert, 13 March 1852

I am recently returned from Fort Rupert, having sailed there
again in January on the SS *Beaver*. Compared to my brief
time there with Wahiya last August, it proved uneventful,
yet equally unfruitful.

The place offered a welcome diversion from Fort
Vancouver. I enjoyed several weeks' relief from botanical
excursions, and I admit, my usual companions. I managed
to reach the Queen Charlotte Islands with others intent on
investigating the possibility of extracting gold, but again, as
we had heard in the reports of others, the Haida were most
unwelcoming. We were unable to reach the shore at all,
their warriors patrolling every possible landing place.

Journal: San Juan Islands, 23 March 1852

I returned to the archipelago yesterday. En route, our ship
passed by a salmon fishery, and we paused to procure some
excellent fish. Now back in Victoria, it is the season to begin
my botanical explorations in earnest.

Juniperus and *Anemone* spp. collected from the island.

Specimen: No. 470, *Ribes*, 21 April 1852 †

Ribes *spp. collected from Vancouver Island.*

Journal: *Abies taxifolia*, 24 April 1852

At last, I have come across a stand of *Abies taxifolia* with seed
in sufficient quantities to merit a collection.

This tree is dominant in the forest where it occurs, having
a magnificent deep crown, with fine sweeping branches that
curve gracefully downwards at their tips. In this way it is not
unlike *Abies Pattonii* which I collected near Mount Baker

last autumn. Its needles are flattened and blunt, striped white underneath, and it seems adept at surviving in deep shade underneath giants of its own kind and those of others. I have seen much of this tree, but so often those in reach are without cones, being in deep shade, or otherwise so high that even my gun is ineffective, although I have tried on several occasions to dislodge a cone-laden branch.

Quite by accident, I found an isolated stand of trees while walking with a friend only a short distance from the fort. For such a large tree it has modest cones which turn yellow as they ripen. I collected a large number of seeds, plus a quantity of partly unripe cones. I have stored them in the same cloth bag my companion had brought along to carry our food and drink. I was quite unprepared for any botanising.

Mr David Douglas recorded this species, but never collected from it successfully. I believe this collection sufficiently important that I will send the seed with a short letter to Prof Balfour without delay, before I depart southwards. This will be my fourth box sent home.

Journal: Summer pastures, 20 May 1852

Mr Ballenden has returned to Fort Victoria on business. We have agreed to travel south from here together, and on to Fort Vancouver, most likely within the span of one week. From there, I intend to conduct a thorough exploration of the Klamath and Cascade Mountains, their slopes being largely unexplored by Messrs Douglas, Lobb et al.

Journal: Fort Nisqually, 16 June 1852

47° 6' 12" N

I am in the United States portion of Oregon. We arrived here by canoe yesterday evening, after an easy passage of little more than 100 miles. The soil around Puget Sound appears to be very fertile, and plant growth everywhere is luxuriant, although the ground near the waterways is often very swampy.

Yesterday evening, Mr Ballenden and I dined with Dr William Tolmie, the chief factor here. Most activity is no longer associated with the fur trade; instead all HBC employees in this place are engaged in farming. There are a large number of sheep being reared on improved grasslands round about, and substantial areas sown to potatoes and tobacco, among other crops, on land between.

I handed Dr Tolmie the letter written by Mr Douglas at Fort Victoria, which confirms he is to furnish me with any supplies required for my professional pursuits. I will store my winter gear for safekeeping at Vancouver, so there is little I need, except a summer bed roll and small cooking items. I intend to travel as far as Fort Vancouver in the company of Mr Ballenden, and from there to proceed alone into the back country of Oregon.

The Journal of Occurrences, Fort Nisqually, 18 June 1852 †

Friday 18 – Fine. This morning Dr Tolmie accompanied by Mr Ballenden and Mr Jeffrey started for Vancouver. Dr Tolmie goes to settle business with Mr Parker. A band of ewes dipped in Tobacco water. Chaulifoux & Cowie handling Hay scythes. Barnes cleaning up Stores. Gang of women clearing in swamp. A good trade in Sale Shop today. Took upwards of $270.00.

Journal: Fort Vancouver, 19 June 1852

45° 37' 17" N

Our party arrived here yesterday; Mr Ballenden's return in particular was marked with a celebratory dinner.

It seems that the fortunes of this place are waning in step

with the fur trade, with much talk round the table being on the subject of farm labour and the difficulties experienced in recruiting good men. Even the Chinese shepherds have decided that gold holds more promise – despite the evident risks – than agriculture.

There is little for me here, so I will depart early tomorrow, my farewells already complete. I will surely miss the company of Mr Ballenden, but it has been agreed I can return to overwinter here at the close of this year's collecting expedition.

Advice, gratefully received, is that I should head south along the Willamette Valley which is, by all accounts, a very fertile area. I will follow the Siskiyou Trail towards San Francisco, which I am told is well furnished along its entirety with inns and hostels, thanks to the great numbers of 49ers who have travelled the other way along this route. Yet I know I will find greater riches by choosing any number of the Indian trails which run from this route, leading me to the firs and pines among the mountains, and no doubt these will lure me from the beaten path.

In my first few steps tomorrow, I will reach the great Columbia River.

Specimen: No. 578, *Lobelia* Sp., 26 July 1852 †

Willamette Valley.

Journal: Umpqua, 15 August 1852

43° 13' 22" N

I did not stay fixed to the Siskiyou Trail for so long. For many weeks I have been following instead the course of the very beautiful Umpqua River, which appears to drain most of the hills in this luscious country, south of the Willamette Valley. Its waters are rich with fish, all of which I have found to be a delight to eat, including a rare sort of bass which has strong bands of black on its flanks and a startling red eye.

Along much of the river's fertile banks, and where the ground is damp among the higher oak woods, is an evergreen tree. A remarkable feature is its glossy leaves that appear not unlike our bay tree in appearance, possessing an attractive smell and strong cinnamon flavour. Its wood is usually yellow, and sometimes a dark brown in older trees which I have seen split open by the wind. In one place I found a grove of the same trees thriving where there had been a wildfire, all having many shoots sprouting from their swollen bases. I believe this to be the tree talked about at Fort Vancouver, which they called myrtle. A farm labourer there told me it has a fine nut which is usually roasted, but I have not tasted one this way – and against this, today, for me they were seeds, not food.

Specimen: No. 610, *Juglandaceae*, 11 August 1852 †

South Umpqua. Evergreen tree, 50 feet high; Leaves lanceolate, bright green above, slightly ferruginous beneath; Bark smooth, ash-coloured. Found growing in groups on the banks of the Umpqua River. This tree has a strong aromatic odour. It is called, by the people in the country, Myrtle.

Specimen: No. 600, *Cruciferae*, 15 August 1852 †

Umpqua Valley.

Specimen: No. 608, *Corylaceae*, 15 August 1852 †

A beautiful tree. Evergreen of a very compact conical form growing on elevated situations in the vicinity of the Umpqua River on red loamy soil. Leaves lanceolate green above, golden coloured on the

underside. It is known in the district where it grows by the name of
Chinkopeen.

Journal: Blue Lake, 22 August 1852

42° 94' 47" N

Leaving the Umpqua River behind, and after climbing
past a series of tumbling waterfalls, I continued my ascent,
seeking a ridge to gain a vantage point. Eventually, I found
myself looking across a most extraordinary lake, high in the
mountains. Its high altitude is the least intriguing of its many
features. The lake sits in a giant crater, its rim reaching at
least 7,000 feet in altitude, being broadly circular and about
5 miles across.

There seem to be no rivers flowing from it in any
direction. The water is the deepest blue I have cast my eyes
upon. For the last two days I have explored its shore. It is a
magical place, where it seems the sky has come to earth, the
clouds scudding across its glass-like surface.

There is a small island to the west, connected to the shore
with a chain of smaller islands. Today, I swam between these
– through a sea of giant yellow water lilies – to reach the
cone-shaped island, for no purpose other than to satisfy my
curiosity. From its shores, I saw what appeared at first glance
to be a man standing upon the water. It moved slightly, to
and fro, and over the space of an hour I observed it to drift
a little. I supposed it to be a floating log which, for a reason
I cannot fathom, hung vertically in the water, its visible part
'standing' about 6 feet tall. It only added to the mystery of
this place.

Journal: Wokas, 1 September 1852

42° 30' 19" N

The same great yellow water lily, which I first saw at Blue
Lake, occurs in great numbers in the marshes here on the

northern shore of Klamath Lake. Its flowers measure up to 4 inches across; its leaves are leathery, and arrow-shaped.

Large numbers of Indians from the Klamath Tribe are harvesting its seeds, filling their boats with great quantities of the pods. They are mostly older women, but there are some younger women and children who work on shore preparing them.

My arrival was met more with surprise than suspicion, even though I am probably the first white man these people have seen, and especially one alone as I am. Mr Peter Ogden is the only man – at least that I know of – who has travelled extensively in this region. I thought I might quietly observe them at work from further along the shore, but my presence was noted immediately; a great shout went out from one, soon to be repeated by others. Two of the female elders approached me in a calm manner, and attempted to converse with me. When it was apparent that this was impossible, they beckoned me with smiles towards the remainder of the group.

We sat together round a fire, and they shared with me a flat bread and some acid-tasting yellow currants they called *chom-chak*. I was also given a healthy portion of a starchy mash which they called *epos*, and my countrymen have nicknamed the 'squaw potato'; it is made from the root of an *Umbelliferae* of some type and has a pleasant nutty taste.

I believe we stared at each other in equal measure.

They wanted to see the contents of my sack, and when I revealed my journal they immediately became excited by my writing marks, and the various botanical sketches, pointing to each in turn, evidently identifying some with their own names and smiling at each other. I showed them my last entry, showing the scene of the Blue Lake, whereupon a sudden quiet rippled through the onlookers, only for it to be replaced a few seconds later by animated conversation. Voices were raised behind me, and before long, a quarrel surrounded me on all sides. One of the men in particular, his face rich with tattoos, seemed gripped by a fearsome mood, first pointing at me, then to the hills and back again, and finally shoving me hard on the chest, whereupon I fell to the ground. Before I could protest my journal was snatched from me, and strong hands prevented me from rising again. I recognised one word repeated time and again in the heated discussion: *giiwas*.

After some minutes I thought I might intervene by attempting to repeat this same word, which I took to be the name of the lake. My attempt had an instant effect in stilling the broil. I boldly held out my hand for my journal (though my heart was pounding), which was returned to me by an elder who seemed anxious to calm the situation, standing between my main adversary and myself. Turning the page, I found my sketch featuring the flowers and seeds of the water lily, and showing this to them broke any remaining tension – '*wokas*,' they all agreed, pointing to the marsh all round us and the innumerable quantities of the growing plant, then the harvest in their laden boats and the seeds in the baskets among us.

I stayed seated on the ground in the hope that they might understand my peaceful disposition. I believe also that the plant seeds and specimens in my possession told them much about the man that I am, and my purpose. Before too long, the men began to drift away, including my adversary (though I noticed with some persuasive handling), and some of the women returned to their toil.

On my part, I admit I thought them an uncommonly attractive race. There was one woman among them who stared at me with rare confidence and was the first to offer me a smile. I felt her young eyes burning my skin, and she made me blush a little, such was the intensity of her curiosity. As is common among many Indian women, her long dark hair was uncut and parted down its centre. She wore it in two tails to either side of her head, and in line with her neck it was gathered in braids decorated with a few small shells and beads. When all the others had returned to work she stayed with me, saying nothing, but always watching. I opened my journal and began to sketch the industrial scene before me, and before long her curiosity encouraged her closer, whereupon she shouted in delight on recognising the illusion. Smiling, she pointed at herself and spoke her first word to me: *Wokas*. I repeated the word, pointing first to the seeds, then to her. Each time she smiled. I had established her name. I then pointed to each of them again and said 'Lily,' which caused her to frown, before she repeated the same.

Still smiling, she went back to work, cleaning the mucilage from the pods to reveal the seeds within. These were placed in open baskets and roasted in batches over the fire. Another of the women was busy grinding roasted seeds, which had expanded and cracked with the heat. She employed a mealing stone against a larger flat stone to grind them, creating a very fine flour. I realised the bread I'd enjoyed was most likely made from the same. I was offered some freshly roasted seeds and they tasted not unlike popped corn.

Last night, I made my camp a short distance from that of the Indian women, whose encampment consisted of domed shelters covered with rush mats. I awoke at dawn, as is my habit, only to be surprised to find 'Lily-Wokas' kneeling nearby. She had raised a small fire and prepared a mint tea which she passed to me, accompanied by another of her charming smiles. '*Machasam*,' she said, pointing at the leaves. She wore a pretty beaded cap, and a thin shawl was draped casually across her narrow shoulders. Her hair hung loose, falling softly over her shawl. I admit that never before had I found a woman's hair so appealing that I wanted to reach out and touch it. I did not possess the confidence to do this!

Today proved to be a day of leisure, as I found myself observing the *wokas* harvest in the constant company of Lily-Wokas, who seemed keen to exchange more words with me. Her lilt made me smile, as each English word she repeated was recognisable, but at the same time quite novel. We went together on a short food-gathering excursion – I noted, always in sight of the elders – along the edges of the marsh and bush of *Salix*. We gathered a large quality of amber berries from a *Ribes* sp. which she called something akin to *lolooyloys*; it looks and tastes very much like our gooseberry.

In the evening my adversary came to see me, accompanied by one of the elders, who wore a great fur hat. When we were sat together, the young man handed me a small woven basket containing lily pods; I supposed they were a peace offering. In return, I offered him an unusually large dentalium shell from a purse about my belt, together with a little tobacco, which he was very much pleased about, if I judged his gruff nod accurately. I learned that his name was Ktaklish; if this were to mean warrior, it would be a deserving name.

The elder attempted to speak with me in a friendly manner about *giiwas*, as Ktaklish looked on. Naturally, none of his words made sense to me, spoken rapidly with a slight whistle through his toothless grin, but his actions clearly conveyed that the place that I had called Blue Lake has some importance to this tribe, no doubt possessing a spiritual significance. I think they might prefer that white men do not disturb this place.

Journal: Comfort, 6 September 1852

Lily-Wokas awoke me, before dawn, by climbing under my blanket. She whispered 'John' in her curious accent, and touched her delicate fingers to my lips to silence me.

We lay for some time together in the dark, her face silhouetted against the orange pre-dawn glow in the eastern sky. I could see she was smiling as she reached out to stroke my hair. She sat to lift her simple shift over her head, before taking my hands and placing them on her nakedness. She was spared my blushes only by fortune of the darkness, yet I felt I glowed so brightly I had surely become the brightest of fireflies in the marshes.

It would be indecorous to write further on these matters, suffice to say that I learned that the Indian woman is quite without any hindrance. It has been a long time since I have lain with a woman, but she took full control of our situation. I drew great comfort from her, as I believe she did from me.

Having fallen asleep after the event, I was surprised at sunrise when Lily-Wokas woke me, and taking me by the hand – to my considerable embarrassment – she proceeded to present me to the others in a way which resulted in much celebration among them. The elders embraced and kissed me in turn, beating my back with bundles of herbs. I think they believe us to be betrothed! Lily-Wokas spoke the name I seem to have given her as though it were another sign, which was greeted with further joyful celebration. I had resolved to continue south today, yet the events of the early morning severely disrupted my plans.

We spent the next two days together in close company. A feeling of discomfort has welled in me as I struggled to decide how to proceed from this place, and how to convey my mission to this young woman. This afternoon I believe she mistook my troubled mind for another mood, dragging me to the water's edge to strip completely and pulling me in after her, whereupon we made love in the lake. She giggled at my hairy torso, shouting repeatedly, 'Mahtah Kagmi, Mahtah Kagmi!' the meaning of which I failed completely to understand.

I spent the hours after an evening meal drawing in my journal, including various maps and phases of the moon, and gesticulating to the sky, in an attempt to explain that I must travel south for perhaps two more months. She said 'Modoc', pointing south, which I understood to be the neighbouring Indian tribe, clearly displaying some trepidation. I believe we finally reached some understanding that I would return when the moon was in its first quarter, two cycles from now.

I have handed her gifts in the form of a blanket, a purse containing a dozen long dentalium shells I had brought from Vancouver Island (I know these to be worth together at least one dugout canoe), and a small knife with an exquisite carved handle. These valuable gifts were well received, but did little to stem her tears.

The next morning, as we shared our breakfast with others, many of the women admired her gifts with obvious envy. I gleaned from their animated talk that my onward travel plans had been explained, and my commitment understood, by the elders. I was showered with food and gifted a bead bracelet for my wrist.

Letter: Post Office to Professor Balfour †

General Post Office,
Edinburgh
23rd August 1852

Professor Balfour
Edinburgh

Sir,

I am glad to acquaint you, with reference to your application on the subject of the postage, that under all the circumstances of the case, the Postmaster General has been pleased to authorise the packet in question to be delivered to you free from any charge.

I am, Sir,
Your obedient & humble Servant,
Fred Godby
Under Secretary

Minutes: Oregon Botanical Association,
24 August 1852 †

Royal Botanic Garden
Edinburgh

George Patton Esq. in the Chair.
Sir W. G. Craig
Sir David Dundas
Mr Charles Lawson
Mr Isaac Anderson
Mr David Smith
Mr John Grieg
Dr Lowe

Mr Andrew Murray, Committee Secretary

The Secretary stated that the meeting had been called to be present at the opening of a Box which had been received from Mr Jeffrey. This was marked No. 3, from which it was to be inferred that another (No. 2) was on the way by some other route. No.1 would probably be the small Box containing botanical specimens and insects etc. collected in March 1851 and received last November.

The Secretary also started that the Box had come from San Francisco by Post, and that the Postage amounted to £135, but that the Post Office Authorities had been pleased to order it to be delivered free of charge, on application being made to them to that effect; and that W. Forbes MacKenzie had kindly aided them in obtaining this privilege. The Meeting directed the thanks of the Society to be tendered to Mr MacKenzie, and requested Mr Smith, through whom the previous communications with him had passed, to convey them to him.

The Box was then opened, when an Inventory of the contents was found at the top, and on examination the contents were found to correspond with the Inventory with the additions after mentioned. There was also found a small bottle and a small box of Beetles, and a specimen of Gold from Queen Charlotte Island. The packages of seeds were all carefully sealed with the seal of the Association.

The Inventory was as follows:

No. 21 *Scilla* Sp.

No. 27 *Penstemon* Sp.

No. 32 *Lewisia Rediviva.*

No. 188 *Penstemon* Sp.

No. 193 *Spirea* Sp.

No. 430 *Abies* Sp.

No. 409 *Picea* Sp.

The Meeting directed that a printed copy of the list should be circulated among the Members, and that the Seeds and Insects should be without delay divided among the Subscribers.

On an inspection of the packages, it appearing that several of them contained so few seeds that it would be impossible to give even a single seed to each Subscriber, the Committee took into consideration the mode of proceeding with regard to them; and being of the opinion that the large majority of the Shareholders, who had subscribed from purely patriotic motives, would that the best means should be taken to secure if possible the raising of every species sent home, they resolved to send a complete set of each consignment to the Royal Botanic Garden of Edinburgh and the London Horticulture Society's Garden.

Article: *Gardeners' Chronicle*, Page 551, 28 August 1852 †

MISCELLANEOUS

Scotch Expedition to Oregon – We learn that at last a box has arrived from Mr Jeffrey, the collector to the Edinburgh Association. Upon opening the box, one or two life specimens of the curious Lewisia rediviva appeared, and a great many fine things. The distribution will occupy much time. Dr Greville, who is not a subscriber, has kindly undertaken that laborious task.

Wool from the Vegetable Kingdom – Two very extraordinary applications of Fir-tree leaves to useful purposes have been made in a domain called the 'Prairie of Humboldt', near Breslau, in Silesia. One consists in the extraction from them of a fibrous material which has been termed 'vegetable wool'; the other in the establishment of medicinal baths with the refuse balsamic fluid, liberated in the course of the former manufacture.

How to Plant a Quick and Privet Hedge – The next point to which we should direct our attention is the preparation of ground for a hedge; and considering the object in view (the formation of a quick-growing and efficient hedge), this ground should be well prepared. Having laid a line...

Letter: James Veitch to Dr Greville, 31 August 1852 †

James Veitch & Sons
Exeter Nursery,
DEVON
31st August 1852

Dr Greville
Royal Botanic Garden
Edinburgh

Dear Sir,

We observed by a notice in the *Gardeners' Chronicle* of the 28th inst. that 'very fine things' have been received from Mr Jeffrey and that the distribution has been entrusted to you. As subscribers from the commencement to the Scotch Expedition to Oregon, and not having had one single thing of any description yet, we beg leave to say that we shall be glad to come in for our share of the 'great many fine things' which have been received. Would it not be advisable that the English subscribers to this undertaking should be regularly informed by circular of the proceedings, instead of being obliged to casually learn what is going on from such notices as may arise in the Newspapers?

We have to apologise for troubling you, even though you were you not a subscriber, as we learn from the same source. Still, as it alluded to you, you will no doubt pardon our at once replying to the fountain head.

Yours respectfully,
James Veitch

Specimen: No. 612, *Pinus lambertiana,* 4 September 1852 †

I am sorry that I have to relate an accident which deprived me of a fine stock of the seeds of this tree. I was encamped one night, and had a small sack of the seeds of Pinus lambertiana *along with me. During the night a ground rat found them out, and appropriated them all, except about two dozen. The season was too far advanced for me to replace them. The few that remain I forward.*

Letter: Oregon Botanical Association to the Subscribers †

7, Nelson Street,
Edinburgh
4th September 1852

Dear Sir,

The Committee of the Association for procuring Seeds, etc. from the western parts of North America, have the pleasure to inform the Subscribers of the arrival of a Box containing a quantity of valuable Seeds, sent by their Collector, and which has reached them through the Post Office.

The Committee have not received any letter from the Collector, but they trust that they will soon do so, together with the Box transmitted before the despatch of the one whose contents come under distribution.

The Committee congratulate the Subscribers on the first packet which they have had to divide, containing acquisitions of so much value and interest as some of those mentioned in the List. The magnificent *Picea Lasiocarpa* Hook., hitherto only known by Sir William Hooker's description, is probably the most valuable of the lot, and the Committee are gratified to find that there're a sufficient number of seeds to allow a complete division. The other plants are also valuable and interesting. Among the herbaceous plants, *Leptarrhena pyrolifolia*, and the very curious *Lewisia rediviva*, particularly deserve notice. If another box, which is supposed to be on the way, turns out as well as this, the Subscribers will have no reason to complain of the collections made in 1851, although this was the least promising part of Mr Jeffrey's route. This year (1852) he was to turn southward, and when the collections made during it shall reach us, there is reason to hope that they may be still more interesting.

I have the honour to be,

Sir,

Your most obedient and humble servant,

George Patton, Chairman

Letter: Oregon Botanical Association to the Subscribers †

7, Nelson Street,
Edinburgh
4th September 1852

Dear Sir,

Since the last was printed, another small package has been received through the Post Office. It is marked No. 4, in the form of a letter, and contains a small bag of Seeds, marked '*Abies taxifolia*'. This has been handed to Dr Greville to be divided along with the rest of the Seeds.

I have the honour to be,

Sir,
Your humble servant,
George Patton, Chairman

Journal: Siskiyou Pass, 14 September 1852

42° 3' 2" N

I have left Oregon and made, at last, California!

It was a long drag after leaving the Rogue Valley, climbing steadily towards the pass which, via a natural notch in the Siskiyou Mountains, offers the main route to the south and onwards to California. A rounded hill, rising to the west of the top of the pass, is known as Ogden Hill, in honour of my compatriot who first crossed here in 1827.

At its highest point, I reached 4,300 feet in altitude. I heard from other travellers that it can be completely impassable from snow for several months of the year. Of more concern was news that, only two weeks previous, there had been a violent skirmish with Indians who are known to prey upon travellers. I did not loiter there.

Letter: Sir William Hooker to Professor Balfour †

Royal Gardens,
Kew,
London
18th September 1852

Professor Balfour

Dear Sir,

I have to thank you for the plants of N.W. America which you have been so good as to send to Kew Gardens. I have already carefully inspected the following species, and the names perhaps of some may not be welcome to you.

I should recommend particularly to the attention of your Collector trees and shrubs, particularly of the *Coniferae*, which are so valuable for our Arboreta and Shrubberies. They have been too much neglected and when collected the specimens and fruits have been imperfect. In Vancouver's Island there are at least four Pines and two Oaks. There is a fine Rhododendron described by Menzies, not yet introduced, *R. macrophyllum*.

In the south of Oregon and N. California is the noble *Castanea chrysophylla*, of which few plants are alive in Europe, and there are three of four Oaks and several Pines, of which at present we know very little.

Your very obedient Servant,
William Hooker

Journal: Shooting Star, 20 September 1852

I have been looking in vain for a flowering specimen of *Dodecatheon*; a rare plant among the *Primulaceae*, but I believe that its season for flowering passed earlier in the year. Local Indians believe it brings them luck in love. There was talk of it among some colonists at Fort Vancouver, believing it a plant I should search for, given its beauty. They called it Shooting Star, on account of its pink petals which trail behind its head, like the heavenly body.

Although unlucky in my search for one in flower, I came across a group of the plants growing on the banks of a stream, although only by chance as they were almost dormant. Their long oval leaves are quite distinctive, being sometimes gently dentate and other times entire. I collected several rhizomes from this perennial which should make propagation possible.

Specimen: No. **601**, *Dodecatheon*, **20** September **1852** †

Northern California. Leaves very long and narrow. Not seen in flower.

Journal: Foxtail pine, 29 September 1852

42° 30' 0" N

The Klamath Mountains are a paradise for the *Coniferae*. Following the Scott and Shasta Rivers, I have explored a good portion of the main valleys and many of their little tributaries, also reaching some of the higher places in the Cascade and Trinity ranges.

Much of this region is dry and rugged, except near the rivers and creeks. There are a great number of birds, large mammals and flowering herbaceous plants that appear to thrive here, accompanied by pines, junipers and cedars as far as the eye can see. I spotted a mountain lion in the distance yesterday; it is a magnificent beast, yet seems to be shy of people. There are many elk.

Near the tree line, even as high as 9,000 feet, there is a particular pine which I believe to be an unrecorded species. It is the most hardy sort, growing in steep stony ground underneath precipices, or on exposed ground. Most older trees seem scarred by every possible misfortune, especially lightning, rockfalls and most especially woodpeckers. Their stems are often without much bark, exposing their white timber underneath. The branches grow tortuously, their twigs thick with needles, resembling a bottlebrush or a fox tail.

If this proves to be a new species I propose it to honour Prof Balfour, namely *Pinus Balfouriana*.

I will continue from this place, following generally the Shasta River upstream, heading further towards its source.

Specimen: No. 618, *Pinus* Sp., 29 September 1852 †

Lat. 40 degrees 30'. Elevation 5,000 to 8,000 feet, found on a range of mountains between Shasta and Scott's Valley, N. California. Leaves 2, 3, 4 and 5 in a sheath glaucous, triangular, 1 1/4 inch long, cones cylindrical, smooth, produced at the points of the branches, generally singly. Branches pendulous and flexible. Bark smooth, of a reddish colour. Timber white, tough and fine-grained. Tree 80 feet high by 3 in diameter. Growing on volcanic debris. *Propose the name of Pinus Balfouriana.

Specimen: No. 750, *Cupressus* Sp., 2 October 1852 †

Banks of Scott's River. Lat. 41 degrees 50'. Growing on sandy soil. Tree 140 feet high, 5 feet diameter. Timber red.

Article: *Gardeners' Chronicle*, Page 630, 2 October 1852 †

GARDEN MEMORANDA

Horticultural Society's Garden, Turnham-Green – The little greenhouse near the carpenter's shop has been newly painted, and the plants – Cape species of Pelargonium, Balsams, and a few other showy things – freshly arranged. This is one of the most useful houses for an amateur with which we are acquainted. The stove adjoining this is gay with Achimenes and Begonias, both of which are brought forward in frames, and introduced as they come into flower. In this way considerable gaiety can be maintained, the plants being at all times removed as soon as their beauty is over. In a pit near this stove was the Society's portion of the Oregon seeds, lately received from Jeffrey, of which some mention was made at p.551 (28th August). They consist of Pinuses and other things which have not yet had time to germinate.

Specimen: No. 706, *Pinus Monticola*, 7 October 1852 †

Trinity Mountains, Northern California; elevation 7,000 feet. Growing on granite rocks on a poor scanty soil. Tree 150 feet high, 1 1/2 foot diameter; bark smooth, grey; timber white, fine-grained, and tough.

Specimen: No.730, *Juniperus*, 12 October 1852 †

Shasta Mountain above the snow line. Growing in fissures and clefts of rocks. 2 feet high.

Specimen: No. 430, *Abies* Sp. 15 October 1852 †

Latitude 42°, Elevation 6,000 feet, Cascade Mountains. I forwarded seeds and cones of this species in Case No. 3 from Mount Baker Range on Latitude 49°, and at the same time suggested that it should be named Abies Pattoniana. *Not having received any tidings of the arrival of that package, I again forward cones which I hope will insure its introduction. It well merits the name I have suggested.*

Specimen: No. 398, *Pinus* Sp., 23 October 1852 †

Mount Shasta, N. California, Lat. 41 degrees 35'.

Elevation from 8,000 to 9,000 feet.

This species I likewise forwarded in Case No. 3. I was not fortunate enough last year to procure a supply. This season I found it more abundant on a snow-capped mountain in N. California 14,000 feet high, its lowest range on this mountain being 8,000 feet, its highest 9,000.

When first it makes its appearance it is a small tree about 40 feet high by one foot diameter with a wide-spreading top, the branches being very strong and much contorted. It dwindles down to a small shrub at the upper part of its range not more than 3 feet high, or a tabular form, so compact that a person can walk along the top of the trees. Found growing near granite rocks where the soil is very scanty.

Journal: A great pine, 24 October 1852

41° 30' 0" N

Yesterday, I collected seeds from the *Pinus* species I first discovered near Fort Hope last year, but there it had held no seeds (No. 398). This time, I managed to deprive *Corvus Columbianus* – or the Nutcracker as Mr Anderson named it – of its feast.

Here in the Shasta Valley, there are extensive groves of another pine of the sort I first observed at higher latitudes, where it sometimes can be found with *Pinus Douglasii*. Yet, in those moister places it is outgrown by that great pine and others, and until today I have been unsuccessful in finding ripe cones and seeds. The smaller trees never produce cones.

At this place, in the foothills north of Mount Shasta, that same pine is the dominant tree. It appears to favour the drier and impoverished soils of the Klamath. The tallest are at least

200 feet by my estimate, and their stems – which smell of vanilla and lemon – grow up to 6 feet in diameter. The largest sort have great dome-shaped heads and this, along with their stature, sets them apart. Their lower branches sweep gently downwards, and often mistletoe can be found in the higher parts. Their needles are bundled in threes and up to 11 inches in length.

Its cones are impressive, as large in size as my two fists together (one I found measured 12 inches in length), and the seeds within are the largest I have seen of any pine. I have often observed the nutcracker feeding on its cones; the both of us eyeing each other in cunning competition. This bird is not unlike our common jay in size, but it is grey all over, except for its black wings and tail, and it has a dagger-like bill. This morning, while making notes beneath the canopy of one of these new pines, I was successful in shooting one; it had alerted me to its presence when winged seeds began to rain down on me. I watched it clutching a yet-unopened cone with both feet, and deftly prise it apart to reach the seeds. I was amazed to find more than 20 undamaged seeds tucked underneath the tongue of the bird. It is skinned and stored ready for sending home in my next box.

Specimen: No. 731, *Pinus* Sp., 24 October 1852 †

Lat. 41° 30'; Shasta Valley, Northern California. Growing on poor sandy soil; Leaves three in a sheath, long pendulous at the points; Cones ovate, produced generally in clusters; Timber yellow, heavy, and tough; Tree 150 feet high, and 4 feet in diameter.

Specimen: No. 746, *Juniperus*, 25 October 1852 †

Klamath. Lat. 41 degrees 20'.

Found growing on desert tracts of country at an elevation of 5,000 feet where there was scarcely any vegetable production, the soil being

almost entirely composed of sand and very dry. The few springs
met with were strongly impregnated with soda. This tree is 40 feet
high with an umbrella-shaped top and sometimes 3 feet in diameter.
Foliage covered with a silvery bloom. It has a disagreeable odour.

Journal: Reunited, 29 October 1852

*Note – here should lie my entry from the 25th inst., which
resides instead inside the front cover.

Following the freak attack, my efforts to attend to my
face wound appear to have been tolerably successful, but
I at once made rapid progress northwards, in fear that if
infection were to set in while I was alone, I may find myself
in a perilous situation. I collected a few botanical specimens
en route, but only when chance favoured me.

Finally reaching Lake Klamath, I followed its eastern
shore, past the place where I had spent those joyous days
with Lily-Wokas, yet there was no sign of her tribe's
summer encampment. I had understood that they would
move from that place northwards to the river, to fish for the
large and plentiful suckerfish.

Along this passage, I passed through several family groups
of Klamath without recognising any individuals. I believe
my appearance unnerved most, but always the beaded
bracelet on my wrist drew gasps, followed by pointed
directions to the north. Clearly it marked my association
with the tribe I sought.

I was unsure what to expect, if, and when, we might
be reunited. I had been away much longer than intended.
Yet I need not have borne any fear, for when the moment
finally came, yesterday, I was welcomed as a long-lost family
member.

A youth I recognised spotted me first as I made my way
along the riverbank, and she ran from me across the fallen
logs and swampy patches with the rapidity which only a
child her age can attain.

Two women elders came to meet me, with a man I took to be the chief among them, wearing an impressive headdress made from woven rushes and fur. After looking at me awhile, studying the wound on my face closely, and talking among themselves, the man introduced himself as Yayna and embraced me. The word *daaslaats* was repeated many times and I took this to be my adversary, confirmed when one of them mimicked attacking claws.

We walked together along the riverbank and, on rounding a final bend, we met Lily-Wokas hurrying our way. She wore the dentalium shells I had gifted her, now strung in an elegant necklace and hanging over her fine clavicles. Her face glowed most radiantly, yet my eyes were drawn to her hand, which she held in a curious manner across her belly. The two elder women came to stand by her, one of whom placed a hand on her belly, and pointed at me with the other. It took but a moment to realise what this might mean. My insides turned and I found myself, for a moment at least, quite immovable. She must have noticed the confusion, if not a little surprise, etched across my face, and she came forward to embrace me, before taking my hands and placing them on her belly. Lily-Wokas was with my child! A chorus of shouts erupted from those round us, which seemed to have grown to more than two dozen within moments.

On reaching their encampment, a poultice – made from the roots of a plant they called *stamak* – was applied to my face wound, and plastered over the top of my self-made stitches, which seem to have served a purpose. It stung fearsomely when first applied, but the throbbing soon quelled. My left hand, which has remained swollen, was dealt with by the elders in much the same way. I was made to drink a warm bitter tea, and this is the last I remember of the day, until waking up this morning.

I am being cared for by Lily-Wokas, who was by my side when I was fully awake, by which time the sun was almost at its zenith. I was very groggy in the early hours, but more than once I felt her rush off, followed by the sound of retching from outside. I fear she is quite afflicted with the morning sickness.

Later in the day she was less queasy, colour once again filling her cheeks. '*Ptishap*,' she has said a number of times, pointing at me and, then, '*muksh*' to the child she carries in her womb. She has made it clear by various signals that her child is also mine, and I can only guess *ptishap* must mean 'father'. She brushed her fingers against my cheek, carefully skirting my wounds, saying with great tenderness, '*Moo ams ni stinta.*' Evidently, she was keen to gain a measure of what this meant to me, and I confess my feelings were easy to portray. I am heady with excitement, now that surprise is finding solace in pride. I placed my hand on her belly and we stared into each other's eyes. Never before have I felt a smile come so naturally, nor be so unyielding.

By my calculation, our child will be born in late May. My mind is racing, and quite overrun with concern, not least in calculating the consequences. What am I to do in these circumstances, and how I can best communicate my intentions to Lily-Wokas?

Letter: HBC to Andrew Murray †

Hudson's Bay House
London
5th November 1852

Andrew Murray, Esq.,
7 Nelson Street,
Edinburgh

Sir,

In reply to your letter of the 3rd inst., I beg to acquaint you that no package from the botanical collector has arrived by the Company's ships from Hudson's Bay. Any collections made by Mr Jeffrey on the west of the Rocky Mountains would not be sent home by H. Bay, but by a vessel from Vancouver's Island via Cape Horn.

I enclose herewith an account of supplies furnished to Mr Jeffrey with accompanying vouchers*, and I remain, Sir,

Your obedient Servant,

A. Barclay

Secretary

* List missing.

Journal: Kapka, 5 November 1852

Under the care of Lily-Wokas, my recovery has been nothing short of miraculous. Even my face appears less hideous, now that my rudimentary stitches have been removed.

There have been several ceremonial moments hosted by the elders, who have made it clear that I am expected to take Lily-Wokas as my wife. We have enjoyed feasts of suckerfish, been made to sit together in the smoke house, and asked to dance together in front of all assembled families. I fear my dancing only makes them laugh, but evidently from joy, rather than any malice.

We have spent every moment together, and our bond is stronger still. With paper and pen, I have drawn two important communication papers. One is a map of the journey I must make to Fort Vancouver, featuring the main rivers, peaks and the ocean. An elder seemed to recognise the latter and much discussion followed; I think this helped establish the distance I must travel. The second is a lunar calendar, featuring the number of new moons and the seasons before I will be able to return. I believe I have reassured Lily-Wokas that I will return before our baby will enter this world.

She has shown much interest in this journal, in my writing and the occasional drawing, which I admit I have no talent for, yet they seem to delight her. She was disturbed by the entry of 25 October on the inside cover. Even to her eyes, my writing must have looked deranged, but the ink smears and drops of dried blood splattered across the page told my story better than any words.

My seeds and pressed specimens have intrigued her even more, and she has attempted to teach me more of her words for some of the plants. *Ktelo* was the name she gave the pine seeds (I had to discourage her from tasting them!). Yesterday, she pointed to a young pine tree, saying, '*ktelo,*' and then, by first depicting a seed between finger and thumb, enacted its growth into the young plant before us, naming it *kapka*. I repeated the word, pointing to her belly, and she laughed. Then she looked at me with a frown spreading across her forehead, falling into silent contemplation.

'Kapka... Kapka!' she said finally, a great lightness shining first from her eyes before spreading into a beguiling smile. And so I believe we have named our child 'young pine'.

I am to leave tomorrow. This is well understood, and I have been shown, by way of maps and signs, where I will find the tribe in May when I must return. By that time, they will be back at the main fishing grounds.

I have determined that the best route northwards will take me first to the west along the Rogue and Umpqua Rivers, following a branch of the Applegate Trail, until I meet with the Willamette Valley, and hence due north to Fort Vancouver.

Journal: Fort Vancouver, 27 November 1852

I have made Fort Vancouver. I was delighted to discover that my old guide, Mr Alexander Anderson, has been temporarily posted here during these winter months, tasked with taking on much of Mr Ballenden's responsibilities while he is busy arranging his affairs before departing to Britain.

It is the first I've seen of Mr Anderson since we travelled together to Fort Victoria. Of course, he noticed at once the scar on my face, and wanted to hear the story of the savaging attack in full detail. I reminded him of our discussion concerning the various beasts, and the relative threats they pose to man. He responded, stating that my case was the first he had ever heard which featured an attack by a mountain lion.

Since I was last here there has been a further decline in the fortunes of this place, with fewer residents and many stores now standing empty. Mr Ballenden confided in me that he thinks the fort may close within a year or two, unless the Indians threaten the region by travelling down the Columbia River, which would instead see it being reinforced. Meanwhile, the HBC has even lost control of some outlying farms to squatter settlers.

I have resolved to keep to myself all the personal occurrences of the last year, even though I consider Mr Ballenden (and to some extent Mr Anderson) a close personal friend. I believe confiding in him may compromise his integrity, which I hold in the highest regard, particularly if he may find himself in direct communication with the gentlemen of the Oregon Botanical Association at some point in the future.

Journal: Mount Jefferson, 4 December 1852

44° 31' 10" N

I am in the foothills of Mount Jefferson, enjoying a short excursion from my winter lodgings, to reach this area of the Cascade Range. The pointed peak itself is clad in ice and snow, but the rich green forests of its foothills remain quite accessible, and are easily reached on horseback.

There are many excellent specimens of a pine that I first observed at lower altitudes nearer to the coast, yet there it is often quite twisted in form. Here, the trees are taller (up to 150 feet), and their stems straighter, though they have the same characteristic contorted needles. It has a handsome domed crown, and its timber looks excellent. I managed to procure cones from some smaller young trees by climbing them.

Specimen: No. 753, *Pinus* Sp., 4 December 1852 †

Collected on Mount Jefferson, Cascade Range. Lat. 44 degrees, elevation 6,500 feet; growing on red stony soil. Leaves solitary or in pairs; sheaths very short, rigid and pungent; cones ovoid, about 3 inches long; Branches verticillate. The leaves from 1 inch to 3 inches long. Tree 20 feet high; 10 inches in diameter.

Email: Arnold Arboretum, Boston, 21 January,
present day

From: helen@arnoldarboretum.org

Hi Ben,

Just to let you know that everything's organised for my visit to RBGE, scheduled for March. I leave on the 11th, and in total will be there for 10 days.

You're right about how nice those guys seem. They've already lined up some trips for me, including to see some 'granny' Scots pines in a nature reserve called the Black Wood of Rannoch, up in the Highlands. Apparently it's a beautiful place, with many unusual birds along with many rare plants and ancient trees. They pointed me in the direction of a picture of that place in *The New Sylva*, which I've seen in the library. I'll check it out – the librarian told me the book has some beautiful drawings in it.

Anyway, I'm making good progress with the journals, now nearing the end of 1852. You might remember, when I saw you at the gala, that I told you he'd met a Native American woman? You'll never guess, though – he writes frankly about her getting pregnant! Also, I've reached the section where his excerpt should be (which describes the cougar attack), and he writes about his recovery thanks to herbal medicines provided by the Klamath tribe.

Best of all, JJ wrote quite a lot about his discovery of the Jeffrey pine (Specimen No. 731). I'll print an extract for you and leave it in your tray.

H.

P.S. Thanks for organising the digital scans. They look great.

Journal: Unwelcome news, 12 December 1852

On returning to Fort Vancouver, I have been dismayed to learn of rumours that placer gold has been discovered along the Similkameen, although I know not where precisely. There is talk that some frustrated 49ers, switching their hopes northwards to the Kamloops and Fraser goldfields, instead strayed up the Similkameen River.

I can only imagine, in place of the beauty of that quiet river, the multitudes of men trudging everyplace with horse and pack animals, their tents filling all the flat land. The place will be littered with fires, their pots hanging from tripods, the air thick with smoke and the noise of industry. There was no further news to be had, so I can only speculate as to its consequences.

And what of my own quiet claim? I am resolved to complete my engagement with the Botanical Association, but in the space of one year I will act upon my own intentions.

As for this place, there are more and more men filing land claims, having reached this as the final destination along the Oregon Trail.

Journal: Mahtah Kagmi, 13 December 1852

At dinner there was talk of giant manlike beasts at large in the Oregon forests. One among us repeated a story, which apparently Mr Peter Ogden likes to tell after learning it from the Klamath Indians.

A young warrior was following a deer trail, but came across a curious sight. The Indian thought at first it was a bush, but on getting closer noticed a strong musky odour; finally realising, when it shifted slightly, that it was not a plant, but an animal. It looked down at him – for it was very tall – with soft brown eyes, every other part of his body being clad in horse-like hair. Being then very afraid, the warrior laid before it a suckerfish he was carrying before slowly retreating. He watched the creature pick up his new meal and run to the timber, leaving behind impressive footprints from his big feet. Soon afterwards, from deep in the woods, he heard a strange echoing call that made him shiver: 'Aaagooouuumt...' Apparently, said the storyteller, the Klamath Indians have a name for it, and absolutely believe it to be a real creature that shares the land with them; they call it 'Mahtah Kagmi'.

'Mahtah Kagmi!' I repeated, rising to my feet before I could help myself. All eyes fell on me in surprise. I recovered enough to dismiss their interest, saying that I too had heard a similar story, but had believed it to be false. Yet the hairs on my neck and back tingled, and inwardly I laughed at the name Lily-Wokas had evidently bestowed on me when we had made love in the lake last September. I retired to bed with happy memories.

PHOTOTROPISM

1853

MOVEMENT TOWARDS THE SUN

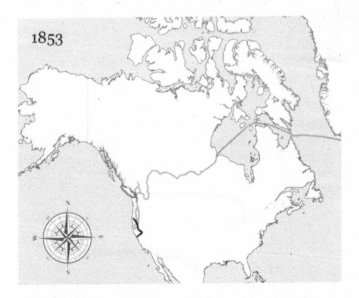

Minutes: Oregon Botanical Association,
12 January 1853 †

Edinburgh

Sir David Dundas in the Chair

George Patton Esq.
Mr Evans
Dr Lowe
Andrew Murray
Mr William Murray, from San Francisco, was also present as
a visitor.

The Secretary explained that no trace of the shipping Box
No. 2 had yet been found, and that no letters had been
received from Mr Jeffrey.

Mr William Murray gave some valuable information as to
the time taken by vessels or packages from Fort Vancouver
to reach this country, from which it appears that there are
few or no vessels which sailed direct from Fort Vancouver
to England, and that goods were usually sent perhaps first
to San Francisco, and then many other places. It was quite
probable that Box No. 2 might still be on the way.

The Meeting, feeling still very anxious both about the
box and Mr Jeffrey, directed the secretary to take steps for
procuring information about them either from the Hudson
Bay Company or other parties.

Journal: Package No. 6, 15 February 1853

A new office of postal services has been founded near to
the fort which postmaster Mr Lonsdale has named Columbia
City. Its opening has prompted me to complete preparations

of package No. 6, containing most of the specimens that I collected last autumn. It will be sent via Panama, crossing overland at the isthmus to avoid the Cape. I am told it may reach Britain in as little as five or even four months' time.

I have wondered myself, on more than one occasion, whether it was this route that I should have followed instead to reach the west coast of America. It could perhaps have saved six months, if not more, of hard travelling, and for most of that distance I might have taken advantage of the plants everywhere about. Instead, my voyage through the cold white desert, following so closely in the footsteps of previous botanists, seemed of little purpose other than to prove my resistance as an explorer. Then again, I would not have been under the wing of the HBC, and I might have been exposed to hardships of other sorts that I cannot imagine.

I feel I have little to write of substance to Prof Balfour, as the specimens and labels are most likely all that these gentlemen are interested in. I have still some other seeds to sort and prepare for sending, and these I will post before I depart south in the spring.

My thoughts are often enveloped by warm thoughts and fond memories of Lily-Wokas, and I find myself distracted, contemplating the new life we have made together, and of the little pine growing in her belly. There is little else here to occupy my mind, other than making plans for this year, which will surely bring new experiences for which I feel quite ill-prepared.

Thoughts of my little Kapka-to-be have only reminded me of my own parents. For the first time, perhaps, I am able to imagine truly what they felt at my departure to this great continent, and, I fear, how my silence since may have so disappointed them.

Letter: John Jeffrey to John Balfour †

Columbia City
15th February 1853
Via New York

J. H. Balfour, M.D.,
Regius Keeper of Botany
In the University of Edinburgh,
Royal Botanic Gardens,
Edinburgh, GB.

Package No. 6

Pinus Sp. No.753. Collected Dec. 4th 1852 on Mount Jefferson, Cascade Range. Lat. 44 degrees. Elevation 6,500 feet. Growing on red stony soils.

Leaves solid single or in pairs. Sheaths very short, rigid and pungent. Cones ovoid, about 3 inches long. Branches verticillate. Leaves are from 1 inch to 3 inches long.

Tree 20 feet high, 10 inches in diameter.

To
J. H. Balfour, Esq.,

Sir,

I forwarded this list of seeds by the United States Mail to New York. The packages I have forwarded by Adams & Company's Express via Panama. Enclosed is Adams & Co.'s Receipt.

I remain, Sir,
Your Humble Servant,
John Jeffrey

Journal: Ready to depart, 12 March 1853

Tomorrow, I depart with a warm heart and a single focus in my mind, namely to be reunited with Lily-Wokas. God willing, I will be in time to witness the creation of our family.

I will be very sorry to part company with Mr Ballenden, who has become a dear friend to me. I feel some considerable guilt at my deceit, keeping my greatest achievement – that of my new family – altogether to myself. I also feel regret, as I know that he would surely have offered very good sense in considering the options before me. Yet I know my secrecy has been the best course to protect him from any questioning by others.

My farewells are complete, yet I hold little affinity with Fort Vancouver itself, which has felt increasingly like a leech upon the flesh of this wilderness and its native people.

I have prepared Box No. 7 and written a short letter to Professor Balfour, which I will send from Oregon City, which lies on my route.

Letter: John Jeffrey to Professor Balfour †

Oregon City, en route for
the Rocky Mtns.,
14th March 1853

To J. H. Balfour, M.D.,
Regius Prof. of Botany
In the University of Edinburgh

Sir,

I forward by mail a small box marked No. 7.

Contents: duplicates of some of the *Coniferae* forwarded

in case No. 5; No. 6 is likewise en route via Panama; No. 8 I have forwarded by the HBC to York Factory, to go to London by their ship this autumn.

No. 2 is gone by Cape Horn.

No. 9 I have made arrangements for sending this case likewise by the Horn. The above number contain specimens of plants, beetles, birds, Indian workmanship, etc., no seeds.

At present I am on the eve of starting for the Rocky Mountains by way of the south side of the Columbia River. On reaching the mountains I will turn south and make for San Francisco. On my arrival there this autumn I hope to have a letter from you giving me further instructions (address J.J., care of HBC Consul at San Francisco, to be called for).

I remain, Sir,
Your humble Servant,
John Jeffrey

Arnold Arboretum, Boston, 28 February, present day

'Hey, Helen, come and join us!'

She spotted him, with arm raised, in her favourite spot by the large window in the far corner, affording the best views over the garden. Helen weaved her way carefully between the tables in the crowded cafeteria, realising she didn't recognise the woman sitting next to him. She was careful not to spill her coffee or smear chocolate gateau on the papers wedged precariously under her arm.

Ben pulled the chair out next to him. 'This is Claire. She's the editor for the member magazine with NPS Oregon.'

With some relief, Helen managed to unload her mixed cargo without disaster. 'That's the Native Plant Society?' she asked, offering her hand.

'That's right, yes,' said Claire. 'It's so good to meet you – Ben's been talking a lot about your work. Sounds like you not only made a great discovery, but you're a pretty useful researcher, too.'

'Thanks. This is such an amazing place to work. It's not just the beautiful plants, but everyone's so friendly.' Turning to smile at Ben, Helen noticed a crumb in the corner of his mouth, but decided against mentioning it.

'Yes, Ben and I have known each other a long time. We were students together at Oregon State, reading botany. I won't tell you how long ago, though!' Claire gave Ben a little wink.

'I've just been reading about Jeffrey's exploits in Oregon,' said Helen. 'He was there from 1851 to '53 – at least, that's what I've found out so far – and he's about to set off for San Francisco.'

'I've just come from the botanic garden there,' said Claire. 'They have such a great collection—'

'Yes, and it's amazing to imagine how it would have been to travel all that way on foot! Oh, I'm sorry, Claire, I interrupted you.' Helen used the moment to take her first mouthful of gateau, savouring the black cherry jam. Mindful of her next appointment, she glanced briefly at her watch.

'No problem. I'm more interested in hearing about your research anyway. So, why is Jeffrey headed for San Francisco?' asked Claire.

Helen took a quick sip of her coffee. 'So far, all we know is that there was an HBC office there, so maybe it was a useful milestone to aim for after exploring the southern part of the Rocky Mountains, like the Cascades, before venturing into the foothills of the Sierra Nevada.'

'And what's the most revealing thing you've discovered?' enquired Claire, picking up her notebook and pen.

'There's a lot about botany, of course, and the hardships of travelling,' said Helen cautiously. She avoided the temptation to keep talking.

'We're being a little careful right now,' interrupted Ben, as if sensing a little tension. 'I'm sure you can appreciate, Claire, that we've just got to play this right. I mean, in terms of letting the Scots into the details before others. All the same, we need to make sure that we get some good profile from this, when the truth – whatever that is – comes out. Helen, tell Claire about your planned trip—'

'Actually, I'm really sorry,' said Helen. 'I've a VOIP call booked with the Scots in five minutes.' She wiped her mouth, hoping to avoid a fate similar to Ben's. Gathering her papers, she stood to leave. 'It was nice to meet you, Claire. I'll get your email from Ben. I'm off to Scotland in a couple of weeks, but perhaps after that I could get in touch? I'd like to learn more about the plants that Jeffrey discovered in Oregon.'

Journal: False start, 16 March 1853

It seems that fate is against me. It soon became evident that my horse was lame, being quite unable to travel any considerable distance, and I had insufficient funds in my possession to procure a replacement without limiting my expedition. Further to this, there is news of violence in the Rogue Valley, and it has been suggested to me by some on the trail that I should delay my departure a few weeks, at which time I might take advantage of the companionship of fellow travellers.

Tonight, I will stay here in Oregon City, and return on the morrow to Fort Vancouver.

Journal: Washington Territory, 24 March 1853

Mr Anderson has been relieved of his position here at Fort Vancouver by Peter Skene Ogden Esq., of whom I have heard so much, and whom I have now had the opportunity to meet first-hand. He is a strong character and does not suffer a fool lightly; many times in his first week here, I have heard him admonishing some unfortunate soul, more often than not an Indian or Chinese labourer. I had rather hoped at dinner that he might tell the story of the Mahtah Kagmi in his own words, but as yet he is more interested in discussing business and politics. I have not the gall to ask him directly.

News has reached us that this portion of Oregon is to be known hereon as Washington Territory, named in honour of the first president of the United States; the boundary with the remaining portion of Oregon Territory, now reduced in size by half, being the Columbia River.

Mr Ballenden departed for Great Britain this morning. I know he intends to call upon his dear wife en route, in the hope that she will travel with him, yet in her recent letters she mentioned being quite unwell. Upon reaching Great Britain, he has agreed to call in person upon Professor Balfour in Edinburgh, to report first-hand about my exploits here.

Journal: Heading south, 6 April 1853

Since Mr Ballenden departed, I have been short of good company.

Today, I collected an advance of $500 from the HBC, which has subsequently secured me a good horse. I admit that I am better provisioned than I was at the start of my aborted expedition last month.

Tomorrow, I leave with a warm heart and a single focus in my mind; our child arrives in this world by the end of next month, so I must travel with haste.

Minutes: Oregon Botanical Association, 14 April 1853 †

Edinburgh

Professor Balfour in the Chair
Lord Murray
George Patton Esq.
John Grey Esq.
Mr Evans
Mr McNab

There was laid before the meeting a communication which had been received from the collector Mr Jeffrey from which it appeared that there were now two separate packages of seeds on their way home.

The meeting, having heard the communication, then resolved that the list of seeds should be printed and circulated among the Contributors and that as soon as the seeds arrived they should be equally divided and distributed, and they appointed a committee to superintend this distribution.

Second, that a letter be immediately despatched to Mr Jeffrey intimating the arrival of the list of seeds, but explaining the surprise of the Committee that this should have been the first communication which the Committee had received for a period of nearly two years, and that it should not have contained any account, either of his past proceedings or of his future movements, and instructing him in future to write separately by every opportunity to account for what he had been doing.

Letter: Andrew Murray to John Jeffrey †

7 Nelson Street
Edinburgh
15th April 1853

Mr John Jeffrey
Botanical Collector
Fort Vancouver

Dear Sir,

We have received your letters dated Oregon 22nd January 1853 and Columbia City 15th February 1853; and, although the boxes you advise us of have not yet come to hand, they will no doubt presently arrive.

In case the different communications I have made to you should not have reached you, I beg to recapitulate their contents. In Autumn last year, I wrote you that we had received Box No. 3 and small parcel No. 4, but that Box No. 2 had not yet arrived; and I sent you copies of two printed papers which were at that time distributed among the shareholders announcing their arrival, and giving information as to their contents. I also mentioned that the Box No. 3 had come by post, and that the Treasury have been pleased to remit the postage and therefore directed you, in future, to send all your Boxes by the British Post unpaid. I further told you, that to avail ourselves of the facility afforded by the conveyance by Post, the Boxes sent should not exceed 2 feet in length, which I suppose means in every way.

The committee were much disappointed that there was no letter in either of the boxes, and that your Journals have not been sent, and that there had been no separate letter sent by post, advising us of the despatch of the boxes.

A month or two later I again wrote you in severe terms, and telling you that Box No. 2 had not yet arrived, and that for want of information as to the ship by which it had been sent, our enquiries after it had been fruitless. Letters to the same effect were despatched to you in the month of February, in which I told you that it would probably be the wish of the Committee that you should continue to explore more thoroughly those Districts where the climate was similar to home. You do not appear yet to have reached the interior range of the Rocky Mountains.

I have now given you a recapitulation of what I have written to you in my former letters. In reference to the contents of Boxes No. 5 & No. 6, the Committee request me to express their pleasure at finding the names of so many good seeds in them, but we hope that the quantity sent will be sufficient to supply all the Subscribers. We particularly call your attention to the importance of having a large supply of such seeds as *Picea, Nobilis*, & *Grandis, amabilis*; *Pinus Lambertiana, Benthamiana, Ponderosa, Monticola, Abies, Douglasii* etc.

In a letter which I had from Sir William Hooker he says, 'I should recommend particularly to the attention of your Collector trees and shrubs particularly of the *Coniferae*, which are so valuable for our Arboreta and Shrubberies. They have been too much neglected, and when collected, the specimens and fruits have been very imperfect.'

We are desirous that you should endeavour to despatch by some of the ships of the Hudson's Bay Company a box with the seeds placed in earth, different layers of which one half-inch thick may be placed between each layer of seed. The box should be 10 inches square and made of 3/4 inch wood. The seeds should be removed from the cones.

As we do not know whether your Journals are in boxes which are coming, it is premature to do more at present than hope you are attending to keep them regularly. You should also advise us of the sums that you find it necessary to draw from the Hudson's Bay Company. We have received accounts from them in which there occurs a charge of a payment of 1,000 dollars to you. You should have written informing us that you had drawn this sum, and the object for which it was drawn. Be good enough to attend to this in future. I need not say more on the necessity of your writing by every opportunity and constantly letting us know where to address our letters to you.

You take no notice of any beetles, which however I hope are also sent in the Box.

We shall write after the Boxes arrive, directed to the same place, and you can leave word so that the letters may be forwarded to you.

I am etc.,
Andrew Murray

Letter: Oregon Botanical Association to the
Subscribers †

Edinburgh
16th April 1853

Dear Sir,

The acting committee of the Oregon Botanical Expedition beg to intimate to the Subscribers that they have just received the following communication from Mr Jeffrey, their Collector; and although the packages mentioned in the letter have not yet arrived, they have thought proper to make known their contents, so far as they have been announced.

The box No. 2 has not yet arrived.

PACKAGE No. 5
  Oregon, 22 January 1853
  Forwarded to Britain by Adams & Co., via Panama.
  Abies Sp., No. 430
  Pinus, Sp., No. 398
  Pinus, Sp., No. 740

Pinus, Sp., No. 618
Pinus, Sp., No. 705
Pinus, Sp., No. 731
Pinus monticola, No. 706

The above is a list of the *Coniferae* in Case No. 5. Besides these, there are seeds of trees, shrubs and herbaceous plants as noted; the greater part collected late in the season, the specimens are poor. In some cases I could not procure seeds.

PACKAGE No. 6

Columbia City, February 1853

Pinus, Sp., No. 753. Collected December 4th 1852, on Mount Jefferson, Cascade Range, Lat. 44 degrees; elevation 6,500 feet; growing on red stony soil. Leaves solitary or in pairs, sheaths very short, rigid and pungent; cones ovoid, about 3 inches long; branches verticillate. The leaves are from 1 inch to 3 inches long. Tree 20 feet high, 10 inches in diameter.

Letter with package:

To J H. Balfour, Esq.

Sir – I forward this list of seeds by the United States' mail to New York. The packages I have forwarded by Adams and Company's Express via Panama. Enclosed is Adams and Co.'s recipe.

I remain,
Sir,
Your humble Servant,
John Jeffrey

Specimen: No. 1061, *Fritillaria* Sp., 23 May 1853 †

Siskiyou Mountains. Flowers bright scarlet found growing upon vegetable loam. Lat. 41 degrees, elevation 4,000 feet.

Email: Royal Botanic Garden Edinburgh, 12 March, present day

From: helen@arnoldarboretum.org

Hi Ben,

I had a smooth flight over, and since being picked up, I've been pampered by the Scots. Last night I ordered haggis from a traditional pub near the garden (I couldn't believe how many whiskies were behind the bar!). It actually tasted fine until I found out what it was made of!

The botanic garden is beautiful, and it's been amazing to imagine J J working here before he started out. I'm pretty sure that some of the wooden floors and narrow stairs in the older buildings won't have changed at all since his time. You can sense the history here, like you said. Yesterday evening I got a weird shiver as I wandered alone along one of the quiet corridors – at the time I was wondering if Jeffrey had ever walked that way. Talk about spooky…!

I've met the librarian in person at last. She brought out a box full of J J materials for me, including the actual minute book of the Oregon Botanical Association. I was amazed when she let me look through its contents without wearing lint gloves or anything. I held letters – the originals –written by J J to Prof Balfour with his signature at the bottom. I scanned the signature with my phone, and it's now my home screen! I can't tell you how I felt, holding his actual letters in my hands after all this time.

This afternoon, I gave an illustrated talk for the RBGE staff. More than 40 of them turned up, which was a surprise, and the small seminar room became crammed full with everyone, from gardeners in their work clothes to the top guy in his three-piece. I must have had more than 30 minutes of questions to answer, and even then they had to cut it short because the room was needed for another event. At the end, I presented the Regius Keeper with the digital copies of the journals that we got bound for them, and he was really, really pleased. Later, I met with him and the head of exhibitions, and we talked through a proposal for a joint project between our gardens, and the idea for a touring exhibition. Sounds great, huh?

Tomorrow, I leave early for the Highlands, which I'm so looking forward to. We're heading first to the Black Wood of Rannoch, as featured in *The New Sylva*, and on the day after, over to Benmore Botanic Garden, which is near the west coast. Have you been?

Anyway, it's been a long day, so I'm off to bed now (still feel a little jet-lagged).

Cheerio the nou!

H.

Journal: A new life, 29 May 1853

I joined my Klamath tribe two days ago, my arrival celebrated with a feast of *c'waam* (suckerfish). The elder women clearly believe our baby is due very soon, although Lily-Wokas, despite her fecundity, has been going about her chores as though the great swelling in her belly is of little consequence. She looks so radiant and our reunion has been joyous; as if we had never been apart for so many tiresome winter months.

There was a time, before my mind was clear on the matter, when I had contemplated having no further connection with these people, this woman, or my future child. I had seen only barriers to overcome and burdens to carry, but my time away only confirmed my own true feelings, and in them I found solace. I wonder whether all the while that I searched for things desired by other men, that I should instead have been looking for something missing in myself. Now, I can find comfort in my own existence, and in my new family which I believe God has blessed me with. I am in no doubt that discovering my own happiness will only increase my ability to satisfy those at home, in one way or another.

It has been made clear to me, by various means, that while I was away other colonists have passed through this country. It is still a rare enough event that the story has been widely circulated and told to me several times over. Somewhere near the Klamath Falls, five men arrived on mules laden with equipment and, by what I can gather from the actions of the storytellers, they set about panning the riverbed for gold. Violence broke out among them with guns being fired, whereupon two died immediately, and two others were badly injured. The single survivor fled on seeing some of the tribe emerging from the bush, leaving behind all their equipment, and I've seen no sign of the two injured.

I am now fortunate by inheritance, becoming the proud owner of all equipment necessary for digging and panning, while several pack animals have been adopted by the tribe. Among the items are a pick, shovels, several wide pans and some mesh screens.

Evening

We are blessed to have a daughter! She had waited for me to be reunited with her mother before she chose to join this world. She has her mother's deep and soulful eyes, as if she has walked in this country before. Perhaps she has shadowed me – wading between the reeds on the riverbank and threading between the pines on the craggy hills, only to catch up with me here. We have named her Kapka; our little pine tree.

The emotion unleashed by the arrival of this new life has quite overwhelmed me. I find myself quite unable to prevent tears of joy flowing freely down my cheeks at regular intervals, even while in the company of others.

I write by the light of a candle, and next to me lies an

exhausted Lily-Wokas, who sleeps with a smile perched on her lips. Between us, nestling in her bosom, lies our Kapka.

Email: Royal Botanic Garden Edinburgh, 25 March, present day

From: helen@arnoldarboretum.org

Hi Ben,

I've got 30 minutes before they take me to Edinburgh airport, and I thought I'd take advantage of the Wi-Fi in the café at the John Hope Gateway here at RBGE.

The trip was spectacular. The hills are beautiful, although the famous heather was not in flower, and I can see why the Scots are so proud of their granny pines. We went to the nature reserve at Rannoch early on the second day, and from the relative warmth of a Land Rover we could hear capercaillies calling. After the freezing mist had cleared a little, we managed to see some, too. The strange birds love to sit in the old pines, often giving away their position by knocking snow off their branches. We also watched two golden eagles overhead.

The gardens at Benmore (linked with RBGE) on the west coast were small but really nice. We had a short walk up a little valley nearby, called Puck's Glen. The guys I'm with said it was the closest they have in Britain to natural conifer forests, like those of our Pacific north-west. The trees are nothing like as grand as ours of course, but it was a beautiful place. You could easily imagine faeries dancing in the little burn (stream).

I've managed to read more of J J's materials each night, and during longer journeys. By mid '53 it seems the Scots had had enough, and were looking to finish the expedition. Trouble is, J J had become quite uncommunicative. Imagine receiving a letter of just a few lines, when you've had to wait six months for a box with material, and almost two years for a decent letter... and then there's the complete absence of journals! Maybe it's being among the Scots here, but I'm beginning to feel for his employers!

Best,

H.

P.S. JJ has become a dad!

Journal: Family, 31 May 1853

Kapka joined us for a gentle stroll through the woods. Swaddled in a blanket, and tucked into a cradleboard made from strips of wood and woven tule, she opened her eyes to stare at me as I walked behind Lily-Wokas on a narrow part of the trail. The sense of three – a family – is a curious feeling which requires significant readjustment of the mind, yet certainly inflates the heart.

Lily-Wokas is remarkably well, given her exertions, if still a little tired. The babe is very content at her breast, and both mother and child have been much cared for by the elder women.

Many gifts have been bestowed on Kapka, among the most valuable being a most beautifully decorated elk-horn purse, filled with dentalium shells. The elder women attended in their best ceremonial dress, tall beaver hats festooned with shells and beads. Laughter and song erupted as the tribe's newest daughter was passed among them for their obvious entertainment and cooing admiration. The principal basket-maker has given us a beautiful creation, featuring a complicated geometric design of diamonds and other patterns. Her daughter made Kapka a detailed little doll, made from the same tightly woven material; it is complete with arms and fingers, and different tones of reeds make its facial features and hair. I noticed Lily-Wokas kiss it before tucking it under the bindings of Kapka's swaddling.

Journal: Forward plans, 2 June 1853

This peaceful existence has given me time to consider, in some depth, my next steps. I have found much succour and friendship among these people, and I admire their simple existence that is so in step with nature and this beautiful country. Yet I fear for their way of life, and even for the people themselves. I have seen with my own eyes the brutality of colonists to fellow human beings, and their disregard for God's other creatures. I am certain there is no future for my family here.

Then, there is my main purpose in this country. I am determined to execute my responsibility with the same enthusiasm with which I started three years ago, or else my achievements will be surely diminished and my reputation tarnished. I need perhaps another year in this continent, with time to complete my work and to prepare my family for all that would be to come, before we decide to travel together to Britain. I wish only that I have earned the respect of my supporters, and that my family will be equipped for life in Edinburgh.

We will travel together to the south, aiming to reach San Francisco before winter sets in. My map suggests that the Sacramento River will provide a promising route for all the distance from Mount Shasta, near its headwaters, for some 400 miles until it reaches the Pacific Ocean.

From the great city we can decide our best course, though I hold some dread for that place, and how we may cope there. For now, I need wait only for Lily-Wokas and Kapka to be sufficiently strong to travel. It turns out that one among the newly acquired pack animals is what I would call a hinny and not a mule, having a stallion as a sire and not a donkey. He looks strong and would be well suited for our onward journey. I am minded to bargain for him, rather than one of the mules, as I have a great amount of equipment to transport, in addition to the family.

Journal: Kowe, 4 June 1853

I have decided upon conducting a short excursion to hunt for more plants while I am in so rich a territory. Lily-Wokas understands my intention and I sense may be relieved to have time without my fumbled attempts at caring for our child.

She evidently spoke about my planned departure with the chief, who came to see me this afternoon. Yayna brought his youngest son, Kowe, and made it plain that we were to travel together. I am quite pleased to have some company, as he is an athletic youth with a great humour, seemingly finding most of my manners highly amusing. I know his presence will also make travel easier among the neighbouring tribes, as he is young enough not to be seen as a threat, and will be able to converse with other *maklaks* (I believe this means tribes other than the Klamath), and even the Modocs.

We leave at dawn tomorrow.

Letter: Professor Balfour to Andrew Murray †

Royal Botanic Garden
Edinburgh
9th June 1853

My dear Sir,

The large box from Jeffrey has arrived. It was sent to my house! and I found it when I came from the Botanical Society meeting. I shall send it to the Garden tomorrow forenoon. You can summon the Committee to meet at the Experimental Garden at 12 or 1, so that we may thus set Dr Greville a-going at once. The earlier we meet the better. Let me know the hour. Send a message to me at the Garden. I have an engagement at the College at 3 1/2 so that you must not be late.

I paid 3/– for the carriage. I sent the money from Mr Smith to you this evening.

Yours sincerely,

J. H. Balfour

Specimen: No. 1124, *Liliaceae* Sp., 10 June 1853 †

Shasta Valley.

Specimen: No. 1113, *Saxifragaceae* Sp., 11 June 1853 †

Found growing on the banks of mountain streams. Lat. 40 degrees. The Indians eat the stalks, when they are young, of this plant. I tried them myself and found them very good. Flowers pink.

Journal: Lampreys, 15 June 1853

42° 13' 30" N

At Klamath Falls there was a great gathering of Indians, evidently from several tribes, given the varieties of costume and appearance on display. They were all there for a common purpose: to gather lampreys.

The only lamprey that I have seen in this country before now was some 20 inches in length and firmly attached to the flanks of a large brown trout. I caught my two-for-one on a makeshift line, sometime last year in a small stream in Oregon. Then, an absence of any real hunger got the better of me, and I fear my eyes won over my belly. The sight of that sucker mouth, complete with its double row of razor-sharp fangs, made me foolishly squeamish, and I threw it back into the river. I admit that my actions embarrass me now, not only for wasting precious food, but for inflicting the teeth of that creature upon another fine fish.

The young men and boys stand right against the raging waters, reaching into the most turbulent currents with wooden hooked spears, with which they try to bring out the lamprey. Others watch the rocks, as these curious fish will swim against the flow and then attach themselves to the rocks with their mouthparts to rest, before continuing their upward journey. I tried my hand at the first technique and had no luck at all, but I harvested many from the rocks. I saw one attach itself to the back of a boy crouching amid the current before a companion pulled it off and threw it into his basket before it could leave much of a mark.

There seems to be no limit to the numbers of these fish, which the Klamath call *gawi*. We left the falls two days ago with two baskets, which Kowe had brought with him, filled to their very brims with the fish. Our arrival at the settlement this afternoon was well received, the sight of our *gawi* harvest bringing much joy before leading to a flurry of activity. Kowe's father spoke to me in words I did not understand, yet I felt the measure of his pleasure at our safe return. Lily-Wokas seemed equally relieved, and I was pleased by her ruddy appearance, the paleness in her face having completely passed.

A great feast of lampreys was prepared. The fish were split in two using bone awls, and each fillet folded like a concertina before being threaded on to giant skewers which were placed upright into the ground around the fire, to cook in the heat and smoke.

Their flesh was very good, once I banished the thought of their mouthparts from my mind, and soon all our bellies were aching. There was much singing and chanting, while others fell asleep where they sat. I remembered then a history lesson from school and the story of Henry I, who if I recall correctly, died from consuming an excess of lampreys. So here I am in Oregon – truly God's own country – married to a beautiful woman and father to her daughter, feasting like a king!

Letter: Oregon Botanical Association to the Subscribers †

7 Nelson Street,
Edinburgh
18th June 1853

Sir,

I have now the pleasure of announcing the arrival of Boxes No. 5 and No. 6, containing a portion of the seeds collected by Mr Jeffrey last autumn, and referred to my communication to you all 16th April last; these were received on the 10th inst., and were immediately put into the hands of Dr Greville for distribution, through whose exertions of the whole have been most carefully divided, and I am able to despatch your share herewith.

The dried specimens have been submitted to Sir W. Hooker and Dr Lindley for identification; and on receiving their reply, their names will be communicated to you. In the meantime, Dr Lindley has mentioned that at least three of the Cones are quite unknown to him.

The Committee of the Association have received further advices from Mr Jeffrey, from which they learn that he has despatched additional Boxes, Nos. 7, 8 and 9. No. 2 (which has never yet come to hand), and also No. 9, had been sent by Cape Horn, but neither of them contains Seeds. Box No. 7, which has been sent by mail, contains duplicates of some of the *Coniferae* now received. Box No. 8 has been forwarded by the Hudson's Bay Company to York Factory, to go to London by their ship this autumn.

Mr Jeffrey's last Letter is dated 14th March, and at that

time he was starting for the Rocky Mountains by way of the
south side of the Columbia River.

I have the honour to be,

Sir,

Your most obedient Servant,

Andrew Murray

Journal: Farewell, 20 June 1853

I believe we both sensed that today was a final farewell,
that there would be no return to this place, and to this
way of life. Yet Lily-Wokas appears ready, almost keen, to
begin our journey together. I found myself thinking again
of Scotland and of my own farewells, from my family and
all those I knew in Edinburgh. I had understood I was to
travel to the New World; I wondered if Lily-Wokas has
the same comprehension, but I think this quite impossible.
I had the benefit of stories from those who came this way
before me, including the great David Douglas. While I and
my sponsors underestimated the challenges I was to face,
I did at least have the advantage of the foundations of an
expectation. I fear that the world to which I will introduce
Lily-Wokas is beyond description, even if I were able to
converse fluently in her language.

While we prepared our baggage together this morning,
Yayna approached us leading the hinny, who wore a garland
of flowers between his furry ears. Kowe rode proudly on the
animal's back, bearing the most infectious smile I have ever
seen. The chief made it clear that the hinny was a gift to
us. He would hear nothing of any of my counter-offers in
gratitude, and was clearly very proud that the gift meant so
much to me.

Later, we experimented as to how we are to travel with
the hinny fully laden, and walk alongside it with other items
on our backs. One of these 'items' will be Kapka in her

cradleboard, of course, who always seems to delight in being carried this way, her eyes taking in all that passes her by. When she is a little older, she will be able to ride the hinny's back, but before then she can be carried as I have seen other babies, attached to an animal's side on their cradleboards.

This evening, we had the greatest feast I've ever witnessed this tribe provide, with guests from neighbouring families bringing food, swelling our numbers considerably. There was an impressive diversity of food, mostly harvested from the river (including more lampreys), enhanced by red meat, which is quite unusual, in addition to root vegetables, flatbreads and nuts.

We danced late into the night, the two of us remaining the centre of attention for the entire evening. For Lily-Wokas, they expressed their love, and I believe asked their spirits to travel with her. For me, I think their attentions were more often focused on the hilarity of my ways of dancing and celebrating, yet I take this only as a compliment among these gentle and resourceful people. They live as the pine, the *c'waam*, the mountain elk, and the mountain lion, each relying upon one another and on other species to survive. These people are inseparable from nature; they are part of the nature.

I am to guide Lily-Wokas from one paradigm to another; I wonder which one will persist through all time.

Specimen: No. 1139, *Lilium* Sp., 29 June 1853 †

Headwaters of Sacramento River.

Specimen: No. 1142, *Erythronium* Sp., 30 June 1853 †

Siskiyou Mountains.

Minutes: Oregon Botanical Association, 1 July 1853 †

Edinburgh

Professor Balfour in the Chair
Sir William Gibson-Craig
Mr McNab
Mr Patton
Andrew Murray (Secretary)

The meeting resumed consideration of the instructions to be sent to Mr Jeffrey.

There are left about £600 to meet Jeffrey's expenses this year and the expense of bringing him home, as his expenses last year had been £350 besides his salary – and could not be expected to be less this year as he was engaged in a more remote and difficult country – taking it at £450 which was probably too little, and his salary at £100. There would only remain £60 to meet the charge of bringing him home and to pay other expenses.

Taking all these circumstances into consideration the Committee were unanimously of the opinion that the Expedition should be brought to a close, and the Association would wind up and be dissolved as soon as the packages containing the results of this year's labours should be received.

The Secretary was directed to prepare a circular to the Shareholders announcing this determination.

Journal: Salmon, 4 July 1853

41° 12' 01" N

We have been following a well-worn trail, the northern sections of which I have already travelled by myself. Now beyond the country Lily-Wokas knows intimately, the landscape itself will no doubt remain familiar to her. Our route took us not too far distant from my previous encampment near Mount Shasta, and perhaps the den of my fearsome foe. Much against my wishes, we were forced to stay overnight, a little further down the same valley. Mercifully, earlier that afternoon we fell in with three women from the Modocs, and we made our encampment together. I feared Kapka would prove but a tasty morsel for my stealthy adversary, and I felt some comfort in our number.

The Sacramento River is guiding us southwards from her headwaters near Mount Shasta, and feeding us as we travel. Today, we stopped for a while near a small suite of rapids, and Lily-Wokas made a large scoop net from pine branches, bound with the bark from a cherry tree. We fished together with little luck, attempting to scoop up jumping Pacific salmon. We had almost decided to admit defeat when a large fish all but jumped in front of us and into the net. It has been the best salmon I have ever tasted, and will feed us for some days to come, once the rest of it has been smoked.

Much of the flora remains familiar, but I have collected a few herb specimens along our route, among them a quantity of seeds from the heads of a species of *Erythronium*. It has finished flowering here, but I have seen its very dainty flowers elsewhere in small numbers; its petals curl elegantly upwards, fading from white to purple, while its anthers are a russet brown and hang downwards.

Journal: Winnemem, 16 July 1853

40° 43' 07" N

Every day on the trail now, we meet at least one group of travellers, either immigrants or prospectors heading north, the latter accompanied by mule trains laden with great quantities of supplies and equipment. Nearly always, both parties will stop and talk, to share news or gossip, and I feel on that account we have nothing of interest to most folk. Tales of gold, violence and women are the most frequent topics of conversation which flow my way. I am usually asked about Lily-Wokas, most people assuming she is my servant, 'companion', or worse. Only if they see Kapka do they realise we are together as husband and wife. Along with her dark hair and brown complexion, Kapka's facial features reveal her shared origins: our Métis child.

For the last few days, I have felt a building sense of despondency. I cannot shake the feeling we are passing slowly through purgatory, from God's creation into man-made hell, and I have little appetite for the company of white men.

Away from the trail, we have encountered people of the Winnemem Wintu, who live mostly along the valley bottoms. Much of their culture seems to revolve around the salmon. Lily-Wokas has had as little luck as I in conversing with them, but this has not been a barrier to us understanding one another by some fashion. We traded some small woven baskets for some food and a blanket; they greatly admired my wife's weaving skills.

Journal: Purgatory, 20 July 1853

40° 38' 05" N

We have passed right through hell's gate, yet have found sanctuary in the most unexpected corner of this country, at the very moment when we most needed it.

Our descent to Whiskeytown, via the creek of the same name, was truly a baptism of fire, into what has become an industrial landscape for the mining of gold. While some of the smaller enterprises toiled with pan and rocker box, other fellows had obviously banded together to build massive wooden-sided flumes to channel the water, from which giant boxes and mats were attached to catch the gold. Many of the men are Indians, recruited as miners.

The entire creek thronged with men, their encampments

filling every flat place; all of them arrived only this winter past, since which the creek has been transformed by digging. Snaking between the workings ran a great flume, carrying away the essence of this place. We made our slow way among them, following the narrow valley, our presence barely turning a head. There was such a riot of clanging, shouting and general bustle, even our steady hinny needed a firm hand to prevent him shying. Even less did he want to pass under the flume where it crossed the main trail, taking a severe dislike to the rushing sound and dripping water from overhead.

Shortly after leaving the creek, we came upon a sawmill, newly constructed. I wondered if timber will be the 'new gold' when all the minerals have been leached from the earth. What then will become of this place?

We entered the centre of Whiskeytown in the afternoon. Already the saloons were full of drunken men, with no less than three separate fights occurring outside one establishment in as many minutes. Passing by a hotel under construction, we made for the general store to acquire provisions, and I forgot myself by strolling in with little thought for Lily-Wokas. The shopkeeper – a little man with a ridiculous moustache and podgy hands – pointed at her, laughing at her obvious reaction to all the commodities on display. I encouraged her to leave promptly and went about acquiring what I needed with as little delay as possible, or at least before my anger boiled over.

Finding our supplies of drinking water very low – hardly surprising given the polluted streams – I looked for a saloon to satisfy our needs. I found a quiet establishment on the outskirts and had only to tiptoe past two passed-out prospectors to order our drinks. There was little choice: either whiskey or water. The story of this place, the barman told me, is that a barrel of whiskey fell from a mule and christened the creek, giving the town its name. I am not so sure it was not on account of the amount of drinking among the miners. I can only think the miners take home very little money, if they come to this town to drink and gamble every weekend. Apparently, the first white woman arrived just one year ago, but now, the barman told me proudly, there were no fewer than four! In this place, I happened upon a copy of the local paper, the *Courier*, dated from April, but being the first newspaper I have seen for many months all of its contents were new to me. I tore out a small section to copy here: 'The mines are very numerous. There is not a river, creek, gulch, or ravine that does not contain gold.'

We left the town without delay, and clearly Lily-Wokas was as relieved as I to put it behind us, yet I knew we were soon to reach the town of Shasta which I imagined to be much the same. The barman described it as being 'cosmopolitan', which I doubted to be true, and I feared we may not pass through it before nightfall. I believe an overnight stay in a town is not yet an option for us, at least until Lily-Wokas has gained more confidence in such places.

After 5 miles, and just before we reached the town, near the north fork of the Salmon River on a small flat, we came upon a man as he worked to construct a small wooden building. His robust rendition of several hymns, delivered in a velvety baritone, alerted us to his presence even before we rounded the final bend of the trail. It was only on drawing near that I recognised, by his plain black clothes, that he was a man of faith. He introduced himself – in a thick German accent – as Father Florian Schwenniger, an Austrian missionary of the Benedictine order.

I do not consider myself a pious man, especially since it has been many years since I prayed in a kirk (if not three years since I attended the little church at Cumberland House), yet immediately I felt at ease in this man's presence. I intended only to pause for a quick conversation, so I asked him to bless our marriage and say a prayer for my family and for our journey. He said he was happy to do so, yet he was a keen talker. Before long he wanted to know almost every detail about my botanic mission, followed by my family circumstances. He seemed to enjoy talking about the trees near his monastery back home in Fiecht, and of their beautiful fruitful gardens, and I sensed it had been some time since he'd had such a conversation. His questioning went on for so long that the sun had begun to set behind the trees, at which point he suggested we make our camp with him and share his food. Lily-Wokas and I both were only too happy to accept his invitation.

During our meal he told me how he was determined to bring encouragement and hope to the miners of Shasta, if not a little order among the Sunday gamblers. Apparently, his presence is so unexpected he has to do very little to gain the attention of the men, who have lately started to help him with his building. And what was he constructing? I enquired. A church of course! It seemed to me that Father Florian was mining the purest form of gold.

Journal: Shasta Town, 21 July 1853

40° 35' 0" N

Shasta Town was every part the abhorrence I feared, and we passed through it as rapidly as we were able, relieved to reach the aptly named Poverty Flats. In the town there had been a large fire only one month before which had destroyed much of the centre of commerce; its construction had evidently been entirely of timber. New buildings were already being erected in almost every place, most of them, I observed, employing bricks.

Father Florian had mentioned that it is not unusual for Indians to raid the town, where they are said to 'stage war dances' in the main street. I noticed that many men carried firearms – even some of those at work on the buildings wore them on their belts – which only leant a further air of despondency to the place. Such reports about the Indians have no resemblance to the Winnemem Wintu that I know, but desperation will make any man do whatever is necessary to protect his way of life, let alone his survival.

Back in the main broad valley of the Sacramento, we soon

reached Clear Creek (sadly it no longer matched its name), which we crossed via a new toll bridge run by a gentleman named Joseph Bell, who lived in the adjacent mansion house (his wealth no doubt arising from servicing the miners). He asked after Father Florian, but nothing about our business.

We have entered a quieter country again, but little of it feels untouched by man. Much of the valley appears very fertile, and crops are cultivated in many places, growing up to the very edge of the Sacramento River which is now a very sizeable waterway. Were it not for my intention to return to the hills for further botanical exploration, I would be tempted to consider switching to a canoe.

Now we have left the hills behind, the heat is more noticeable, becoming quite intolerable at midday. Today, my thermometer stood at 96° in the shade. Lily-Wokas has woven a bonnet to attach to Kapka's cradle, keeping the fierce sun from her face.

Journal: Relief, 23 July 1853

The trail is easy-going and, knowing well the countenance of our hinny, Lily-Wokas has decided to mount Kapka's cradle on his flanks, facing sideways in front of our baggage. This has the advantage that we can orientate her to avoid direct sun at different times during the day. She seems surprised to see both her parents walking alongside, and when the motion has not caused her to sleep, she has been smiling at us and gurgling.

We have elected to avoid the main trail, preferring to weave our way along the smaller paths. It seems a great relief for Lily-Wokas to be free of the weight upon her back. She has had noticeably more energy, often gathering herbs, and sometimes leaving our path to explore further afield.

The abundance of food and warm climate make this an agreeable country.

Journal: Sierra Nevada, 25 August 1853

39° 01' 39" N

Father Florian's blessing has parted all before us over the last few weeks. I have thought little of collecting plants, and been even less diligent in keeping this journal. Deliberately travelling just 10 miles or less each day has allowed us to enjoy all the simple comforts that this country provides.

Lily-Wokas is making excellent progress in learning more of the English language. We play word games as we walk, pointing to things all around us or mimicking actions. I am a little ashamed by the scant progress I have made in learning Klamath in return, but it is more important that Lily-Wokas gains some proficiency by the time we reach San Francisco.

Kapka enjoys lying on her blanket when we pause to rest or eat, and likes to reach for her little doll and kick her legs. She smiles at every opportunity, sometimes squealing with delight, especially if we hold her near the hinny's nose.

Rising out of the ever-widening Sacramento Valley is a curious range of hills known as the Marysville Buttes. These marked the end of our gentle meandering and I chose this point to leave the main valley behind, heading eastwards towards the ridges of the Sierra Nevada. We skirted the northern slopes of the Buttes and I was surprised that they disappeared almost before they had begun, extending only 10 or so miles in all directions. The trail immediately became more demanding, yet still feeling quite refreshed after the previous weeks, we took it in good heart.

After descending to the Feather River we began our long ascent into the Sierra Nevada. The terrain became more exacting as we climbed, and progress ever slower. It is a very beautiful country, rich with alder, oak and pines, their shade providing welcome respite from the heat. I elected to follow the north fork of the American River (which my pre-war map labels as the Río de los Americanos), along which we have been ascending for the last two days. The canyon has become ever more enclosed.

At the place where we now rest, its walls tower over us by some 2,000 feet, while the river tumbles in a never-ending series of rapids, echoing thunderously off its walls. The clear turquoise waters are cold, and rich with rainbow trout. It is a paradise, but we can go no further, the trail having become very arduous for the family, and impossible for the hinny.

Journal: Eldorado, 11 September 1853

38° 41' 47" N

After turning back from the ravine, we have headed generally in a southward direction, probing any promising valleys running west to east towards the summits. All have proven unsuitable after some distance.

Now below 39° latitude, this is the furthest south I have yet explored.

We find ourselves in a vast forested area. There are a great many pines of the same species that I discovered near Mount Shasta, but with them there are now also firs, oaks and a wealth of unfamiliar herbaceous flowers. There are very few people here, except occasional small family groups of Indians harvesting acorns.

We surprised two old prospectors yesterday who had made their encampment in a lonely place. In conversation they mentioned the name Eldorado for this region.

Specimen: No. 1336, *Penstemon* Sp., 18 September 1853 †

From Sierra Mountain, Lat. 39 degrees, elevation 8,000 ft. Growing upon decayed granite.

Journal: Summit, 25 September 1853

38° 50' 53" N

I have made the main summit of the Sierra Nevada. This is

the first time I have ever paused to write at such altitude, yet this is also the first time that I have climbed a peak and not been subjected to extreme cold. The opposite is true here, the sun's rays being very intense.

Four days ago I left Lily-Wokas and Kapka, together with most of our provisions, in a beautiful sheltered place, and did my best to explain my purpose. It is now a little easier, thankfully, to communicate with one other.

The view from here is spectacular, it being 9,000 feet in altitude at its peak, and once attained it felt as though I stood on the roof of the earth. The ascent on the western flanks was tolerable, although the density of scrubby trees and rough granite made progress a little tedious. On the lower slopes, there are many rich alpine meadows. Above them the trees continue, almost to the summit itself, yet immediately on the east aspect there are very few trees until far below. From my elevated position I can see a very large body of water orientated north–south, surrounded by forest on all sides, its water as clear as a crystal. It is as though a portion of the sky has landed in the forest. There are many hundreds of smaller mountain lakes dispersed across this country, but this is the largest I have seen.

Everywhere on the summit are beautiful alpine plants, among them most notable a *Mimulus* with very pretty pink petals and a yellow throat.

Specimen: No. 1475, *Juniperus* Sp., 25 September 1853 †

Summit of Sierra Nevada Mountains. Tree 20 feet high, 2 in diameter, growing on granite rocks. Altitude 8,000 ft. Lat. 39 degrees.

Specimen: No. 1477, *Mimulus* Sp., 25 September 1853 †

Found on the summit of the Sierra Nevada Mountains.

Specimen: No. 1480, *Abies amabilis*, 29 September 1853 †

From near the summit of Sierra Nevada. Lat. 39 1/2 degrees, altitude 7,500 feet, growing on clay soil.

I climbed a great many trees without succeeding in getting good seed of this tree; all the cones seemed to be destroyed by frost before the seed was matured. Tree 3 feet in diameter, 200 feet high growing in dense forests, bark rough similar to the bark of A. nobilis. Young trees covered with balsam blisters.

Specimen: No. 1481, *Pinus* Sp., 1 October 1853 †

Sierra Nevada Mountains, growing in barren sandy places. Trees 15 ft. high, 1 ft. diameter.

Journal: Nisenan, 2 October 1853

38° 39' 29" N

After a fond reunion with the family – Lily-Wokas would not release me from a deep embrace for many minutes – we packed up the girls' makeshift encampment, and began our slow descent together from the mountains. Finally, and a little reluctantly I admit, we began our long journey towards the great city of San Francisco.

We are in the territory of Indians known as the Nisenan. They are a peaceful people and have made us welcome at all times. They eat well, carrying more flesh than most other tribes, and dress in highly decorated robes of feathers. The village where we now find ourselves is near the Sacramento Valley, and without exception is the largest Indian settlement I have seen, having at least 500 people living permanently together. It is testament to the fecundity of nature here. In the mountains, the settlements are smaller, typically of one or two families who live by harvesting game, fish, plants and seeds. The Nisenan gather acorns from the oak forests and store them in purpose-built huts for the purpose of grinding them to make flour, and this sees them through the winter months.

Near the Río de los Americanos, which is followed by the main trail, there are signs of gold mining at almost every turn. In the foothills yesterday we came across a monstrous sight: a Nisenan family settlement had been put to the flame, the charred remains of the buildings and other structures half-standing among blackened trees. From the limb of a great oak were lined up a man, woman and three children – all of whom were prepubescent – swinging from ropes about their necks. The birds had already had their fill of the softer parts. I was unable to console Lily-Wokas, yet our anger gave us the energy to take them down and provide them with a decent burial. My prospector's shovel felt like lead in my hands. Even though I knew I was fulfilling God's will, their wretched souls watched as I wielded the white man's sickle, and I felt sick to my bones.

I fear that most miners care nothing for these peaceful people, reacting unquestionably with violence, prompted merely by hearsay and rumour spat among them. I have taken care to disguise the panning equipment on the mule, as it will only provoke fear and suspicion among the Indians. We have not communicated the gruesome discovery to our hosts, as it would most likely lead to an outbreak of violence, if not a war in the region. If this were to happen, there would only be one outcome for these people, and I admit to a little selfishness in also fearing for the safety of my family in these circumstances.

Journal: Squaw man, 3 October 1853

On the trail today, I experienced the first prejudice shown to me by fellow white men, who seeing me with Lily-Wokas openly abused me by shouting 'squaw man' as we passed by a saloon. By this I understood they mean a white man who lives, not only with an Indian, but as an Indian. I can only imagine that, in my weary travelling guise, it may indeed appear as though I have been deep in the country for most of my years.

I think it was of little harm, however, as on hearing my retort in a Scottish accent, the two farmers seemed surprised by my countenance, quickly leaving us to ourselves. I was tempted to return the insult by using a fitting derogatory term that I first heard at the Fort last winter – that of 'rednecks'; but I resisted, not wishing to start a fight.

Journal: Hinny, 4 October 1853

38° 33' 20" N

As we approached the city of Sacramento, which sits at the confluence of the American and Sacramento Rivers, the trail became thronged with travellers, including large numbers of cattle and their drovers. I had already come to a decision that we must part with our dependable hinny, which I found most regrettable; but we had no alternative. He has been reliable over so many miles, carrying a great and often priceless weight upon his broad back and steady hooves. Less difficult was a decision to rid ourselves of all gold-prospecting equipment; in fact I want nothing more to connect me with this evil. My only regret is that I brought it with us this far on our journey before attaining such enlightenment.

The roads on the outskirts of the city were lined with traders and I found little difficulty selling either, bargaining a good price for both commodities, especially the prospecting tools, which are evidently in strong demand. I admit I shed a small tear as we walked away from the hinny; foolish, I know, but she has been part of our family and much loved by Kapka.

Most of this town, like so many with wooden buildings in this hot country, has recently been terribly affected by fire, but unlike others this one has also suffered winter floods. Construction work is found everywhere, the streets laid out in very straight lines. We walked down the very broad J Street towards the docks on the banks of the Sacramento, heading towards the tall masts of a couple of brigs, moored next to countless schooners. Only on nearing the docks could we see the lower profiles of two steamships, these being ferries working from this place to San Francisco.

Lily-Wokas became very withdrawn among all these people, her fearful eyes often catching mine before darting between the strangers thronging round us. I can only imagine what she felt, though the terror was plain to see. I took her arm in mine, and so we walked together towards the boats and their towering masts and slapping cables. I realised they must have appeared to her in every way to be an alien entity, so wholly different from any nature known to her.

We took our time approaching, so that my poor wife had time to absorb, at least, a little of what she saw. Finally, having secured our passage from the ticket office, we discovered we had a wait of several hours before the steamer departed. Not wishing to remain in so busy a place, we explored the vicinity, hoping to soothe Kapka, who had become unusually restless. Almost at once we came across a very unexpected sight in this hot city – huge blocks of ice being cut by a gang of men, working in pairs with two-handed saws, as though they were working on the butt of a large tree. A giant sign bearing the name 'Sitka Ice Co.' was fixed over the warehouse entrance, and below it in a smaller garish font, 'Importers of Alaskan Ice'. Lily-Wokas was fixated by the scene, while my mind was trying to digest the concept of ice being imported from Alaska. While we gawped, a worker handed us both a fragment of ice, providing wonderful relief from the oppressive heat.

Journal: San Francisco, 7 October 1853

We arrived in the heart of the great city yesterday, and I have since been busy making good a great number of arrangements. I feel I have walked most of the streets in the process.

The final stages of our journey here were remarkable. From Sacramento, we headed down the meandering river for several miles on the steamship, crowded with immigrants, traders and others. As we reached a large bay, I admired freshwater marshes of tule extending along its shores as far as my eye could see. It is the first vessel of this sort that Lily-Wokas has travelled on, and she was quite terrified by every aspect of it. Kapka evidently sensed her fear and was impossible to calm by any means, crying so loudly that everyone on the ship stared at us.

We had to change ships to cross San Pablo Bay itself, boarding the *Hector* steamship, which was powered – according to the Captain, who shouted proudly over the din – by an old sawmill engine. I had found a little free space standing next to the wheelhouse. He leaned over to enquire as to my business, noticing, as many do, that I do not have the typical appearance of a miner. He laughed, saying that he was in a similar trade: the ocean sailors have a name for those who ply these inland waters – that of 'tule sailor'.

Kapka again became quite inconsolable on this vessel, as she had the last, but then the strangest moment came upon us. She suddenly fell silent and I thought perhaps she had at last cried herself to sleep, but I noticed she was wide awake, yet completely stilled. A murmur rolled across the ship until the news reached us, too, that we should look to the starboard.

We were passing through the deepest part of the bay, and

alongside us breached two gigantic whales. They followed us for some distance, keeping quite close and on the same compass. Lily-Wokas was, for once, not the only person agog at a new sight. I believe I was among the few people on board who had witnessed before the scale of similar beasts first-hand, but I was no less impressed by them. She asked me their name and I tried to explain that they were not fish but creatures that breathed air like mankind, but she shook her head, in disbelief or wonder I am not sure. The silence that fell upon Kapka was quite unsettling, and beyond any explanation.

We have found lodgings close to the waterfront, off Mission Street, in a busy place full of traders of all sorts, but I believe the landlord to be a trustworthy sort, and I think we will remain untroubled here. The bed was the first that Lily-Wokas had seen and it amused her greatly to lie in it, why exactly I am unsure, but she used the word 'soft' and seemed happier than I have seen her for some time. As I lay beside my girls this evening, I found I could not sleep. The inn at Gravesend – where I stayed before setting sail from England – came to mind. It was quite a shocking recollection, having never thought of it again since. The only things in common between these two places are the throng of people, the noise and the smell of a busy seaport.

I have risen early from bed to write this entry, and it gives me some satisfaction to have a desk again, and to gaze upon my family sleeping nearby. I believe it important that my personal circumstances are not known by anyone working with the HBC, and certainly not by those with any links to the Oregon Botanical Association. I must be careful not to be seen in my wife's company in certain places. I also need to ease Lily-Wokas gently into this tumultuous society, and that will not be an easy task. It is a shocking place even for someone as well travelled as myself. Most of the population is made up of young men; if an army were conscripted from here, there would be only a handful of old men and boys left behind. On the streets there are beggars everywhere, and most of these desolate people are women and young children, most probably left behind by prospectors, who will, most likely, return worse off than when they left with such high hopes.

I located the HBC office this morning; it is a tiny concern with none of the bustling stores and mass of men found in its Goliath coastal bases further north. After sharing my credentials with the indifferent clerk, I was successful in withdrawing a banker's draft for £200. He was a Scot – the first I have conversed with for a long time – and having finally struck up a conversation, we agreed to meet for a drink to share news of home. From there, I visited bankers Page, Bacon & Co. to cash the cheque. The money will cover our winter lodgings, food, new clothes and miscellaneous stores.

This afternoon, near the waterfront at 90 Sacramento Street, not far from our lodgings, I was fortunate to find, quite by chance, a small fabric store named Levi Strauss. The German owner by that name furnished me with some excellent workwear to replace my tattered clothes. I told him that the last German I met had been Father Florian, building a church at the boundary of the mountains, seemingly teetering at the edge of civilisation itself. Evidently, he was known to Mr Strauss, who told me the priest had been sent there by the city's Archbishop Alemany.

After this, I walked along the waterfront to the offices of Mr William Murray in Montgomery Street, only to discover that he was absent on business.

*I belatedly recalled that I had a beautiful specimen from the *Liliaceae* in my sampling bag, collected several days ago from the banks of the great river. It seems none the worse for my ineptitude in not preparing it in my usual fashion.

Specimen: No. 1485, *Liliaceae* Sp., 7 October 1853 †

Banks of Río de los Americanos.

Journal: Filthy rich, 10 October 1853

This city seems to be built with gold dust. It is said that if you lick the back of your hand before washing and retiring to bed, you will gain a golden tongue by the morrow. Signs of money are evident in so many aspects, from the bold architecture to the attire of the very rich, who appear to mill about with not a single care for any work or purpose.

The old timber houses, so affected by the last fire, have mostly given way to brick and stone. On Montgomery Street, there is a new bank under construction, using granite imported from China, no less. In time, I think this will be a fine city to rival others I have seen. Yet San Franciscans are in the habit of throwing rubbish of all sorts into the middle of their streets, even their finest thoroughfares and squares, creating piles of clothes, boots and broken crockery mixed with rotting fish and old meat. These stinking piles appear to move by themselves, so ridden are they with rats, although by each morning only the inanimate items remain.

Mercifully, we are fortunate to have two excellent ratters resident at our lodgings. I am supplementing their killings with a little extra from our larder in payment for their services. One has taken to lying on our windowsill, where she grooms herself in the fall sunshine, and purrs in contentment. Lily-Wokas has warmed to her, and the two seem to have arrived at a comfortable level of mutual trust.

Journal: Telegraph Hill, 10 October 1853

Leaving our lodging together and following the quieter streets, we made our way to Telegraph Hill this morning. I intended to gain a view of the city from this vantage, and provide an opportunity for Lily-Wokas to consider our civilisation from afar.

For some considerable time we sat in silence, our backs against the semaphore tower, while I let her absorb the sights before us. In the distance, beyond the bay, rolling hills surrounded us on three sides of the compass, and to our west, the huge expanse of the Pacific Ocean. The enormous natural harbour in the foreground was crowded with ships (I have heard that often they must wait several days to unload), their forest of masts testament to the importance of timber to man, not least among these supporting the trade in precious metals. Every flat area of land around the bay already boasts a building, and even the zone destroyed by the great fire two years ago has already been developed. I have spoken myself with a wharf owner who was in the process of filling it in to reclaim it from the sea, as he plans to sell the land as new building plots.

I pointed to the north-east, from whence we'd come, and said simply, 'Klamath country.'

She turned to me and I saw then the tears in her eyes. She wept for a long time, her head buried against my chest, sobbing until my heart melted. There was simply nothing I could say. I shared in her despair – for absent family, for death and destruction of all that is good and beautiful – and felt only misery for the plight of this former paradise.

Letter: Professor Balfour to Andrew Murray †

Dollar
Clackmannanshire
13th October 1853

My dear Murray,

I see that Hooker in his Kew Journal for this month is down upon the Oregon Committee. He has made a mistake in the matter. The Document is not a *published book*, meant as an *authority on Science*, but a mere private catalogue sent to the Oregon Subscribers. He had no business to get one. It was a matter of favour and this is the way he thanks us. It was not intended for criticism. The new, or supposed new, plants we are well aware have not been determined because most of them were imperfect and without many seeds.

The Committee meant to attach merely provisional names which could be changed afterwards without any difficulty when the plants are fully determined. I think the Committee should not have put names. That was my opinion from the first and I merely yielded on the understanding that the printed document was to be considered a private one and that the names were to be noted as provisional. Numbers would have served our purpose well. Mr McNab was afraid of the nurserymen attaching their own names. All that the Committee were anxious to make known were the *Coniferae* which had been given drawings, along with notes by me in regard to them. The cones were all I examined. The other unknown plants were not touched because in most cases they were not capable of being determined accurately in their present state. We were waiting for an opportunity of having them described and with figures (if new) in Hooker's Bot. Magazine.

He must suppose that we meant to become *authors as a Committee*. The words 'Oregon Com.' were put at the end of the hazarded names for the *express purpose* of showing that there was no *particular botanical authority in the matter*. For my part I would not have put my initials to any, except to some of the *Coniferae* which I examined.

Do you think it is necessary to write to Hooker? If so we can talk it over when I come to Edinburgh.

Yours sincerely,

J. H. Balfour

Letter: George Gordon to Andrew Murray †

Horticultural Society Gardens,
Chiswick, LONDON
18th October 1853

Professor Balfour
Regius Keeper
Royal Botanic Garden
Edinburgh

Dear Sir,

I return you many thanks for the coloured copy of Jeffrey's *Coniferae* and at the same time to apologise for not having done so sooner, but I deferred it until I had examined its contents, and compared the figures with Douglas and Hartweg's specimens. I now give you my opinion upon the names given to them.

Pinus Jeffreyi is quite new and very distinct. It comes nearest to one called *P. Torreyana* by Dr Asa Grey, from the same Country.

Pinus Flexilis is very distinct and new.

Pinus Balfouriana is distinct and new.

Pinus Murrayana, this is the same as *P. Muricata* Don. and *P. Edgariana* of Hartweg.

Picea lasiocarpa is the same as *P. amabilis* of Douglas.

Abies Pattoniana is quite new and very distinct.

Thuja Craigana is the same as *T. Gigantea* of Nutal and *T. Menziesii* of Douglas and is No. 1972 of Hartweg's Specimens.

Abies taxifolia of a former set is *A. Canadensis*.

Trusting you are quite well,

I remain, Dear Sir,

Yours truly,

George Gordon

Journal: Liquid gold, 1 November 1853

Yesterday evening, I met with James, fellow Scot and new acquaintance from the HBC offices.

We talked of home for many hours, during which time we visited several bars, and I fear I became quite inebriated. So little whisky has touched my lips for most of the year that I found I had little, if any, tolerance. It was only my fear of talking freely about Lily-Wokas and my family that kept me from utter shame.

Lily-Wokas had no sympathy on my return home, but I have little memory of it.

Journal: A modest celebration, 14 November 1853

I tried to convey to Lily-Wokas that today was my birthday (27 years), but she found my explanation inconceivable and I was forced to abandon any attempt at it. Instead, I prepared us a meal with unusually good meat, and gifted her some freshly picked flowers. I toasted my own good fortune, and relished her happiness.

Journal: Black walnut, 20 November 1853

Today, I made Lily-Wokas laugh. We had again escaped the city, as we have tended to do as often as we are able, this time to explore the woods along a length of unspoiled shoreline of the great bay. There was a small island, separated from the mainland by only 40 feet of water (though I soon found that it was deep), and growing on it stood a group of trees of considerable interest. They appeared not only to be of the same variant of black walnut that is common in the wet woodlands around the bay, but also to have some fruits still hanging from their branches. I can only suppose that their island status offered protection from those animals that usually feast upon them.

I stripped to my undergarments and, before Lily-Wokas had an opportunity to react, I dived into the water and made my way across. I could hear her screaming as I swam, only to start laughing uncontrollably when I staggered on to the far shore, water dripping from my drenched clothes. I danced for her, which only delighted her further, before climbing some of the trees to shake free a torrent of their nuts. I can only imagine how ridiculous my sodden figure must have appeared as I 'attacked' each tree.

These *Juglandaceae* are related to the black walnuts I have seen in the hills but seem to be completely without the hairs underneath their pinnate leaves, which otherwise look very similar. The other difference will be their liking for wet ground, which the other seems to despise. The form of these black walnuts is very variable, sometimes multi-stemmed almost from the ground and more of a shrub, other times having a tall branch-free stem, and being overall a majestically tall tree.

Specimen: No. 1489, *Juglandaceae* **Sp.,**

20 November 1853 †

Bay of San Francisco.

Minutes: Oregon Botanical Association,

23 November 1853 †

Edinburgh

Professor Balfour in the Chair
Sir William Gibson-Craig
Sir David Dundas
George Patton Esq.
Mr McIntosh

Mr McNab
Mr Andrew Murray (Secretary)

The Secretary stated that the Hudson's Bay Company ships from York Factory had lately arrived, but that they had not brought the box of seeds announced by Mr Jeffrey to have been sent by them – neither had any letter of communication been received from him.

Taking into consideration the non-arrival of this package, and the neglect of Mr Jeffrey to communicate with them, it was agreed necessary to obtain information on these points from some other quarters.

They therefore directed the Secretary to apply to Mr William Murray, presently in San Francisco, and request the favour of his seeing Mr Jeffrey on his arrival in San Francisco. They also resolved to invest him with full power and authority over Mr Jeffrey to dismiss him if he had misconducted himself, or to re-engage his services for the new association if one was set up.

They accordingly instructed the Secretary to write to Mr Jeffrey to place himself entirely at the command of Mr W. Murray, and to write two letters for Mr W. Murray. One to be in gentle terms and to be used as his warrant for engaging Mr Jeffrey, and the other authorising him to dismiss him, stop his cheques and take possession of the seeds and articles belonging to the Association, should he prove contumacious, or should he find on examining into matters he ought to be dismissed. The Chairman and Secretary were directed to sign these letters in their official capacity.

Letter: Peter Ogden to Andrew Murray †

Vancouver
Washington Territory
7th December 1853

Andrew Murray, Esq.,
Secretary
7 Nelson Street
Edinburgh

Sir,

Your favour of 7th March last only came to hand on the 26th November without any enclosure mentioned for Mr Jeffrey, and I have the pleasure to inform you that the package left here by that gentleman for transmission to Scotland was despatched from this place on 1st November to Victoria, Vancouver Island, from there to be sent to London by one of the vessels of the Hudson's Bay Company which will probably sail about the end of this month.

Mr Jeffrey left here last April to proceed overland to California; we have not heard of his arrival in San Francisco. The last account we had of him was from Crescent City, a town on the coast to the South of Umpqua River. Before leaving, Mr Jeffrey was supplied with five hundred dollars for which I hold his receipt, and in the event of his not returning here this account will hereafter be handed to your company.

I am, Sir,
Your most obedient Servant,
Peter Skene Ogden
Chief Factor, Hudson's Bay Company

Journal: Kit Carsen, 13 December 1853

In a saloon this evening, a small book – known here as a 'dime novel' – was passing hands with some excitement. It depicted the exploits of a so-called mountain man by the name of Kit Carsen. I do not know whether this is a man of fact or fiction, but if I ever meet him I'm unsure whether I could control my rage.

I have never felt such disgust by anything printed on paper. The writing told only of derring-do against Indian 'savages', while the pictures unashamedly depicted this man murdering natives with axe and knife, and all the while he made his fortune by mining gold. He seems to hold a particular hate of the Blackfeet, whose territory I passed peacefully through with Wahiya east of the Rocky Mountains.

I am quite ashamed.

Journal: Sawmiller, 21 December 1853

I happened, by chance, to meet and fall into conversation with a sawmiller while I waited to be served at a store. The odour of pine and resin gave his profession away, even though he was freshly dressed.

Outside the store we talked at length, for he showed considerable interest in my purpose, all the while sheltering from a torrent of rain under the cover of a sagging awning. On learning about my possible intentions to travel east, he mentioned many fine timber trees growing in an extensive forest north of the headwaters of the Gila River in New Mexico. Among them, by his account, are some very fine ponderosa pine, which I know is of great interest to those at home after being introduced by Mr Douglas (and I recall noted with enthusiasm in Lawson's *Agricultural Manual*). He was only able to offer scant information about the region when pressed.

Back at our lodgings I have consulted the map, but it is of little aid. A range of mountains are shown north of the Gila River, which flows east to west, over which the word 'Apache' is printed to indicate the territory of the Indian tribe by that name. I recognise that such a trip will be quite impossible with my family, yet I grow restless. I am in two tortured minds as to whether I make arrangements to leave them here while I travel, or simply abandon all notions of further exploration.

BLOSSOMING

1854

DEVELOPMENT OF A
REPRODUCTIVE STRUCTURE

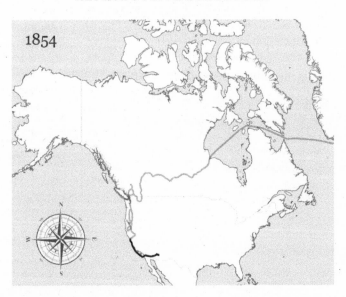

1854

Letter: William Gibson-Craig to Andrew Murray †

Riccarton
East Ayrshire
5th January 1854

Andrew Murray, Esq.,
7 Nelson Street,
Edinburgh

My dear Sir,

Jeffrey is indeed a most extraordinary fellow, and his conduct is utterly incomprehensible. He must however have received your letters to him letting him know how much we were dissatisfied with his conduct, and your brother must also have seen him, as the Consul would probably give him notice of Jeffrey's arrival, and make the latter aware your brother has been enquiring for him. The next mail must therefore bring us accounts of him in one way or another, and if these are not perfectly satisfactory, not a post must be lost in directing your brother to dismiss him immediately and stop his credits, or he may again be beyond our reach and drawing for any sums he chooses without our knowing how or where the money is to be spent.

  I am,
  Yours very truly,
  W. Gibson-Craig

P.S. I am much better but not allowed to leave the house in this weather.

Journal: Box No. 10, 5 January 1854

Yesterday afternoon, I called at the premises of shipping company McKinlay, Garrioch & Co. which is not far distant from here, being situated at 116 California Street. After following a dizzy maze between crates of English soap, printing paper, Scotch whisky, linen, pig iron and London stout, I finally came to their offices at the rear of a busy warehouse. I learned that the box can travel via Panama, and may take only eight weeks or so to reach Britain, and the clerk informed me the next shipment is scheduled to leave tomorrow. I immediately secured transportation for it.

Overhearing small talk concerning my business, and the possibility of travelling to New Mexico, another clerk appeared to be well informed about the so-called Southern Route. This man being near the end of his shift, I offered to buy him a drink in exchange for more information.

His account of the Southern Route described an excursion that would involve considerable hardship, including the crossing of arid mountain ranges and plains, not to mention the avoidance of warring Indians, even before the upper Gila and it forests would seem within reach. The route which most of the 49ers and others have since followed, in reverse, is from this city via Los Angeles, San Diego and then eastwards via Fort Yuma towards Colorado. Yet he told me also that the port of San Diego is within easy reach on board one of the many Pacific Mail steamships, which now offer frequent sailings. From there a journey of some 200 miles east over the arid mountains will see me to the fort situated below the mouth of the Gila River. For these reasons, such an expedition appears more feasible than it might have done just two years ago. At least I have more information, which I can now ponder.

Afterwards, I returned post-haste to our lodgings in order to complete preparations of Box No. 10. I have written a short letter to accompany the seeds and specimens collected during my southward journey this last year. There may be fewer items than in previous shipments, but the diversity of the collections, especially those from the Sierra Nevada, will no doubt please the subscribers.

Lily-Wokas surprised me by having a meal ready on my return, having gone alone to both the butcher and general store for provisions, and evidently succeeded in communicating with the men who serve in these places. I almost wept with happiness for her success. After we had eaten, and the dishes cleared, she came and sat next to me and whispered, 'Here, I have baby,' catching me utterly by surprise as she drew my hand to her belly. Then my tears flowed, and we embraced one another.

Journal: An enquiring mind, 19 January 1854

This evening, I met again with James from the HBC office. This time I was more hesitant with my consumption, although he cared little for his own sobriety.

I believe he must think me slow, for he seemed keen to ask a great many questions about my travels, perhaps because the topic of Scotland had dried up; yet I offered little information, save for the main cities of my expedition that I had reached in their turn. When he pressed me about my exploits across the wilder parts of the country, I merely summarised my botanical exploits and academic pursuits. He was keen to hear about any experiences with Indians, but I responded by saying that I had never felt threatened; this is quite true, of course. He did not anticipate an account of falling in love and of fatherhood, so none was offered.

We talked also of my future plans, and I mentioned my consideration towards travelling up the Gila River and into New Mexico. He suggested I employ Adams & Co.'s express to communicate with the HBC, as they have an agent in San Diego who deals with the Southern Route.

Letter: William Craig to Andrew Murray †

Riccarton
East Ayrshire
25th January 1854

Andrew Murray, Esq.,
7 Nelson Street,
Edinburgh

My dear Sir,

It is most extraordinary that there is even by this Mail no letter from Jeffrey, who must a month before it was despatched have received all your letters. You must call a meeting of the Committee that we may consider what is to be done.

I have not been so well for a few days and shall not be in Edinburgh this week, but any day after Monday next I will endeavour to attend it.

The neglect in despatching the box from Columbia City is most provoking, and the contents will probably be useless.

I am,
Yours very truly,
W. Gibson-Craig

Letter: John Balfour to Andrew Murray †

2 Bellevue Crescent
25th January 1854

Andrew Murray, Esq.,
7 Nelson Street,
Edinburgh

My dear Mr Murray,

There is at present in Edinburgh a gentleman by the name of Ballenden who saw a great deal of Jeffrey when he was at Fort Vancouver, and who is anxious to give us information regarding him. I think that it would be proper to ask him to attend a meeting of the Committee whenever Sir Wm. Gibson-Craig is better.

Mr Ballenden's address is 28 Hamilton Place. You might communicate with him on the subject.

By the bye a Dr Vienna is very anxious to exchange beetles. Mr G. Lawson will give you the particulars.

Yours sincerely,
John Balfour

Letter: John Ballenden to Andrew Murray †

28 Hamilton Place
Edinburgh
1st February 1854

Andrew Murray, Esq.,
7 Nelson Street,
Edinburgh

Dear Sir,

The notes which you saw yesterday were merely extracts from my own letter book, and referred to several dates when I saw Mr Jeffrey. They were written down yesterday morning before leaving home. The substance of these were – Mr Jeffrey came out by one of the Hudson's Bay ships to York Factory, wintered the following season partly at Cumberland House and partly at Saskatchewan. In the spring of '51 he crossed the mountains (via the Athabasca River), descended the Columbia as far as Fort Colville, and thence rode and boated to Fort Langley on Fraser's River. From thence he crossed over to Vancouver Island in the latter part of summer. During the remainder of that season and the spring of 1852 he remained at Vancouver Island, occupied, as I understood, constantly in Botanical and Geological researches.

I met him in May '52 at Nisqually near the head of Puget's Sound, and took him with me from thence to Fort Vancouver on the Columbia River. He remained with me until he had completed his necessary arrangements for San Francisco.

I have no note of the date of his departure, but I think it must have been some time in the month of August. He remained at San Francisco I believe only one day. On his voyage to California, he visited the northern part of that state, and examined I believe carefully the valleys of the Umpqua, Klamath and Rogue Rivers, and while at Fort Vancouver his researches were I understand extended to the Cascade Range. He remained with me from the time he returned until 24th March 1853 when I left for England. So far as I saw, no person could be more painstaking or indefatigable and notwithstanding that appears to me now inexplicable, I feel perfectly confident he will give full satisfaction to his employers. Mr Douglas's address is (if private) James Douglas Esq., Hudson's Bay Company, Vancouver Island; (if official) His Excellency James Douglas Esq., Governor of Vancouver Island.

I understood from Mr Jeffrey that some botanical specimens had been forwarded to England by him from York Factory; in '51 from Vancouver Island after reaching that place, and from Fort Vancouver by Express. If this can in any way be of service to you I shall be most happy, as I feel very anxious respecting the fate of poor Jeffrey, knowing well that if he followed up the route hinted to me he had some dangers of no very trifling nature to contend with.

I am, dear Sir,
Yours very truly, John Ballenden

Journal: Smallpox, 24 January 1854

My darling wife, my Lily-Wokas, has smallpox. I thought
at first it was a common cold, but soon afterwards she
developed a very bad fever and dysentery, and just days later,
the terrible pustules erupted across her face, arms and legs.
Her eyelids swelled so much she could hardly see. She was
admitted yesterday to the Smallpox Hospital, but already the
light has faded from her eyes. Kapka has gone with her to
that terrible place, as she too has early signs of the affliction.

Like most immigrants, I received the vaccine when I was
young (I was then 14 years old).

I wish, with every part of my being, that it was me lying
prone among the dying, and not my darling girls. I am quite
helpless.

Journal: Smallpox, 25 January 1854

Lily-Wokas passed this morning. And with her, my unborn
child.

Kapka was vaccinated immediately on admission, but
since then she has developed a fever. I only fear the worst.

My wife was taken away to be buried, I know not where,
and I did not see her. This may have been a small mercy.
I have seen others near their end, when the disease is thick
upon every inch of skin. I have attempted to fight such
images from my mind.

Journal: Smallpox, 29 January 1854

By some miracle Kapka's fever has died a little, and so far she
shows no indications of the pustules upon her skin.

Arnold Arboretum, Boston, 28 March, present day

The beautiful orangey dark-brown swirls of Ben's office door came into view. She knocked gingerly next to the fingerplate – 'Black walnut *Juglans nigra*' – careful not to spill the coffee down her cream skirt or on to the shiny parquet floor.

'Come in!' He always had to raise his voice to be heard through the heavy door. 'Ah, Helen, great to see you. Take a seat… let me move these papers for you.'

Helen settled into the squeaky leather chair, allowing its padded wings to envelop her. At least the effects of jet lag weren't as bad as when she flew to the UK; not that she'd slept much on the way home.

'Thanks for the report,' started Ben, who seemed keen to make it a brief meeting. 'I gather you had a really productive time.'

Helen leaned forward, deliberately making herself a little less comfortable. 'Yes, it was a great trip, and I've got so much material to work on now, alongside the journals—'

The ring of the phone made them both start a little.

'No, I'm with someone right now, may I call you back?… I see… Give me five minutes? Thanks.'

'Would you like me to leave now?' Helen asked, realising that she should have booked their meeting.

'No, it's fine, really,' said Ben. 'In any case, it's not often that I have a real-life drama unravelling before me – it's a wonderful antidote to some of the problems I have to deal with here. And in case you're wondering, it's never the plants. Always the people!'

'OK then,' she said. 'I couldn't sleep much on the plane so I got a lot of reading done, both his journals and most of the archival material from RBGE. So much happened to Jeffrey in '53… drama, adventure and tragedy. He scaled the Sierra Nevada. His wife died of smallpox; it was so sad to read. And he turned his back on gold. The way he articulated his feelings seemed so… well, like a modern-day environmentalist, I suppose.'

'And do the archives still back up his journal entries?'

'From what I've read, they match perfectly. Letters from him in '53 are short on content and detail, but the plant records still support everything.' Helen reached into her bag for some papers. 'But there's another dimension to all this, too. It seems that there were plenty of frustrated subscribers back in Britain, plus in-fighting between some of the key players. Oh, and they actually dismissed him too. The organising committee asked for a notice to be posted in a local newspaper. Look what I found when I searched the online archives of a Californian paper earlier this morning…'

ALTA CALIFORNIA

Advertisement: *Daily Alta California,*
4 February 1854 †

Nevada County Gold Mining Company—Stockholders in the above Company are hereby notified, that a meeting of the Trustees, held at San Francisco January 24th, an assessment of $5 per share was levied on each share of the capital stock of said Company, payable immediately, at the office of Henry S. Fitch, Treasurer, No 157 Montgomery Street.

By order of the Trustees. E. S. Curtis, Secretary
N.C.G.M.C.

John Jeffrey, Collector for the Oregon Botanical Association, if in San Francisco or the neighborhood, is hereby requested to call at the office of W. Murray, 170 Montgomery Street to receive a communication from the Society.

Guano Charters,—The undersigned are authorized to charter vessels to load guano at the Islands of Chincha for ports in the United Kingdom of Great Britain, Ireland, and on the Continent.

ALSOP & CO.

'Imagine sending bird droppings all that way back to Britain!' said Helen.

'That's incredible – the notice of recall from the society, I mean!'

'I know, right? But there's more. I found an extraordinary letter in the RBGE archives between the Murray brothers – you may remember, Andrew in Scotland, William in San Francisco. It seems that they may have been quietly plotting a botanical expedition of their own! In the same letter, there's some really funny lines, including mention of 'H. B. Majesty', presumably meaning 'His Botanic Majesty', namely Balfour.'

'Ha!' exclaimed Ben, glancing at his watch.

'Look, I'd better go,' said Helen, standing to leave. 'I'll send you a copy of that letter.'

'Sure. By the way, I've heard from the Scots. Seems they were impressed by your research, and by you. We've discussed the joint exhibition idea, and we've agreed to see if we can get some joint funding. If we're successful, might you like to be involved, potentially as the curator?'

'You mean, you might offer me a job?'

'Sure, we'd be lucky to have you on board. If only everyone was so easy to work with...'

Helen skipped lightly over the parquetry, dashing past rows of colourful botanical prints. Notices of forthcoming seminars and field trips, pinned loosely to the corkboard, settled in her wake as she stepped out into the warm spring sunshine bathing the garden.

Journal: Childcare, 12 February 1854

My existence is barely tolerable. I have no appetite for food, nor life.

The wife of my landlord is helping to care for little Kapka, who has at least has been discharged from the hospital. I am thankful for God's small mercy.

I know not what I must do; either for Kapka, or with myself.

Journal: Company, 1 March 1854

Finding me still morose, or as he put it, 'completely at sea', my landlord suggested I seek company. Recognising that he meant well, towards the end of the day I called upon James at the HBC office, hoping for a little solace. Yet I was quite unable to find any, thanks in no small way to my previous secrecy concerning my personal circumstances. There was nothing I could say with him. I told him that I had been ill for some weeks, hoping this might explain my manner, and that now I was beginning to plan in earnest for the continuation of my explorations.

Journal: A small fortune, 15 March 1854

My landlord offered me unsolicited advice the other day: that I should consider leaving Kapka in an orphanage, being of the opinion that raising a child is impossible for a single man, or otherwise I should get married without delay.

I already knew he was right, having reached the same conclusion, but neither course of action seemed feasible. The only orphanage I have seen in this city – quite by accident – was an abomination, with the children living in squalid dormitories and seemingly short of any stimulation, let alone any education. As to the latter – the idea of a marriage – my grief so overwhelms me I cannot even imagine such a thing.

A fortune of a sort was gifted to me this morning, when I returned to Levi Strauss's store to purchase a pair of trousers. I intended only to make polite conversation, yet he was clearly surprised to see me alone with my baby daughter; and in response to his kind words, I found myself sharing partial news about my predicament. He told me he had donated an undisclosed sum of money, alongside other local philanthropists, for the construction of a new orphanage to be run by the Protestant Orphan Asylum Society. Apparently, it is due to open next week (on the 22nd) and he said he would be pleased to introduce me to the ladies who will manage it.

Journal: Orphanage, 16 March 1854

I went at once this morning to the new orphanage at the junction of Haight and Buchanan Streets, beyond the western outskirts of the city. After meeting with two ladies from the society's management committee, I was afforded a tour of the fine stone building, which from its elevated position looks down on the city. It has two large dormitories and is equipped with very good sanitation, benefiting also from good air and natural light.

Few questions were asked about my circumstances, and Kapka has been accepted with minimal bureaucracy and no expectation of payment. I believe that Mr Strauss has played a considerable part behind the scenes to make this possible.

This only leaves my heart, which I fear is not only broken, but shattered into countless pieces. Were it only possible for me to arrive at a better solution, I would give up anything to reunite my family, to be with my Lily-Wokas again, and for circumstances to be as they once were. She was a wonderful mother and I have let her down, and I have failed my daughter.

Minutes: Oregon Botanical Association,
23 March 1854 †

Royal Botanic Garden
Edinburgh

Present:
Sir William Gibson-Craig in the Chair
James McNab Esq
Andrew Murray, Secretary

The Secretary stated that he had heard from his brother Mr William Murray in San Francisco, who had received the instructions and authority sent him to examine and enquire into Mr Jeffrey's proceedings, and to deal with him as he might find proper according as his examination might turn out, but Mr Murray has been unable to find Mr Jeffrey. In his letter he says 'I called at the British Consulate and enquired for Jeffrey. There are letters for him there but they do not know where he is. I have left a written request for him to call on me immediately on his arrival in San Francisco, and when I see him I shall attend to your instructions regarding him,' and in a postscript Mr. Murray adds 'since writing this the Consul has told me he had heard that Jeffrey was in San Francisco but did not know where to find him. I have accordingly inserted an advertisement in the Alta California, a copy of which paper I have addressed to Dr Balfour.'

From this it appeared that Mr Jeffrey had never called for his letters at the Consulate in San Francisco, although it was there that he directed them to be sent. It appeared, from the date of the Bill for £200 lately received, that he had been in San Francisco on 7th October. From Messrs McKinlay & Garrioch's letter to Mr Lawson, it appeared that he was in San Francisco about the middle of November. From the time when Box No. 10 was received at Panama it must have been despatched about the beginning of January, and from the letter above quoted it seemed probable that Mr Jeffrey was still there at its date (25th January) and all this time he had never addressed a single line to the Association or any of its members. No journal had been found in any of the boxes sent by him, and no information had ever been given as to his proceedings, his expenses, his intromissions, or any subject! The quantity of seeds sent home in Box No. 10 was so exceedingly trifling for a year's collecting that it was obvious that Mr Jeffrey was not discharging his duty to the Association in this respect either.

Taking all these things into consideration, as well as the whole tenor of his conduct to the Association, *the Committee unanimously resolved to dismiss Mr Jeffrey for neglect of duty*, and they wished the Secretary to communicate this to Mr Jeffrey himself, and also to the Treasurer Mr Smith, to the Secretary of the Hudson's Bay Company and the factors thereof at such stations as Mr Jeffrey might be expected to visit, and to acquaint these gentlemen that his credits were withdrawn and recalled and that the facilities and privileges which they had been instructed to give him were no longer to be afforded.

The Secretary was also directed to request Mr William Murray to receive over from Mr Jeffrey anything belonging to the Association which was in his hands, and to take the necessary steps to stop Mr Jeffrey operating upon the credits with which he had been furnished, by advertising his recall in the newspapers etc., and should Mr. Jeffrey have left San Francisco, Mr Murray was requested to endeavour to trace him, and get his dismissal communicated to him as speedily as possible.

The Secretary was also directed to take the necessary steps to interpel the paying away of the money which had been paid to Prof Balfour and Mr Bayley on account of Mr Jeffrey's yearly salary and to secure it for the protection of any person on whom Mr Jeffrey may pass a draft, should he hereafter do so, or for payment to the Association of any balance which may appear to Mr Jeffrey on a settlement of his account; and he was designed to affect this by getting a letter from Prof Balfour and Mr Bayley, or if that failed, then he was instructed to have recourse to legal proceedings to arrest it.

It was also resolved not to proceed further with the scheme of continuing the Association for another year, and the Treasurer was directed to return the subscription for this purpose which had already been received.

The Secretary was directed to take the necessary steps for winding up the Association as soon as affairs were in a position for this being done.

Journal: A most terrible deed, 23 March 1854

My darling, my precious Kapka, may God bless your waking hours and forest dreams.

In a little purse tucked among her blankets, she carried the Similkameen nugget, with a short note in my hand. It is a meagre token of my gratitude to the orphanage, and a poor measure of my culpability.

I left her with the ladies before distress completely disabled me.

Letter: Oregon Botanical Association to the Subscribers †

BOTANICAL EXPEDITION TO OREGON

> 7 Nelson Street,
> Edinburgh
> 24 March 1854

Sir,

The Committee beg to inform the Subscribers that another box of seeds has arrived from Mr Jeffrey, which they have lost no time in getting divided by Dr Greville, and the Share falling to you is sent in a separate package.

The Committee regret that neither the quantity nor the state of the Seeds sent on this occasion is such to give them satisfaction; and they are under the necessity of stating that lately, Mr Jeffrey has not paid that attention to their instructions which they were entitled to expect, and they have, therefore, thought it right to abandon their intention of keeping him out for another year; and the money of those gentlemen who have already contributed for this purpose will be returned to them,

I am,
Sir,
Your most obedient Servant,
Andrew Murray, Secretary

Names of Plants of which Specimens or Seeds have been received from Mr Jeffrey in Box No. 10:

No. 740 *Pinus muricata*? A few cones as specimens. (Seeds bad)

No. — *Primula* Sp. Headwaters of the Sacramento River (72 shares)

No. 1475 *Juniperus*. Summit of Sierra Nevada Mountains (120 shares – seeds each)

No. 1489 *Juglandaceae*. Bay of San of Francisco (45 shares – 2 seeds each)

No. 1490 *Abies grandis*. Sierra Nevada Mountains (92 shares)

Letter: HBC to Andrew Murray †

Hudson's Bay House
London
27th March 1854

Andrew Murray, Esq.,
7 Nelson Street,
Edinburgh

Sir,

I am directed by the Committee and Governor of the Hudson's Bay Company to acknowledge the receipt of your letter of the 23rd inst. respecting Mr Jeffrey, your botanical collector in Oregon, and to inform you that, in accordance with your desire, the necessary instructions will be given to the Company's Agents in North America to discontinue granting him any further allowances or privileges. I am however to state that as these instructions cannot get to hand for some months to come, and it is possible that Mr Jeffrey may in the meantime receive advances from the Company's stores. The Governor and Committee will, in such a case, consider your Association to be liable for the same.

I am, Sir,
Your obedient Servant,
W. G. Smith
Assistant Secretary

Letter: Sir William Hooker to Professor Balfour †

Royal Gardens,
Kew
29th March 1854

Professor Balfour

Dear Sir,

I cannot say much in favour of many other specimens of this set of the Californian plants.

I send you a result of the best examination I can give them, but it cannot be so satisfactory as if the specimens were more perfect. Many are very good things.

No. 1116 – *Penstemon* – This I think new and allied to my *Penstemon Wrightianus*.

No. 1478 – it is really impossible to speak with certainty of Pines from small single specimens. The leaves and cones vary so much. In many respects its cones are near sample 740, but the leaves are longer and slenderer and the spine on the scales of the cone.

The rest of the Nos. in a day or two.

Truly yours,
W. J. Hooker

Journal: Fort Yuma, 28 April 1854

32° 43' 55" N

As the clerk from McKinlay, Garrioch & Co. had informed me, I believe my passage via steamer to San Diego must surely have saved me considerable effort compared to the overland route from San Francisco. I sailed on the SS *Southerner*, the ship being full of miners returning from the north.

Even so, once back on land, the 220 miles east of the city were a little arduous. Travelling on foot with only what I could carry on my person, first I crossed a small range of mountains. These created their own clouds by mercy of their elevation (I made 4,400 feet), and harboured a rich mix of pines (more of No. 731) and various hardwoods, though I had no way of collecting from them at this time. Afterwards, I descended to the plains, which were mostly barren, except for the valleys which in places were quite verdant. The last 50 miles were most disagreeable, passing through an extensive desert with large shifting dunes. I had only a small amount of food with me, and could only trudge from one watering place to another. One important place was 'Cooke's Wells', a pair of wells that must be re-dug by every traveller, as the sands are always filling them in. I know now that I am much better suited to the harsh cold of the north than I am to this heat.

Now that I have made Fort Yuma, it took no time to recognise there is little to keep me here. I have already explored what little green life exists about the fort, yet I admit I still have little interest in plants. I can only hope that time given to exploring on my own will revive my botanical enthusiasm.

The buildings sit on a small promontory just below the confluence of the Colorado and Gila Rivers. Unlike the forts in Oregon, this appears not to be a defensive settlement but a station where troops are based, from where they patrol the surrounding area to dissuade Indians from causing any mischief among passing immigrants.

I keep a low profile and have not mixed with the officers who run the fort. As I travel lightly, I need only to secure a mule and a few further provisions before I can continue up the Gila River. This river once marked the border with Mexico, but since the so-called 'Gadsden Purchase' of last year, it simply marks a green corridor through the territory of New Mexico, and my route to the Gila forest.

Only in fitful dreams do I find any comfort in memories

of Lily-Wokas and my little one. When we are together so, life is fleetingly complete; like a precious spark from my flint, keeping me alive in the coldest north. Every perspiring dawn is the cruellest bolt to the heart.

Letter: Peter Ogden to Andrew Murray †

Vancouver,
Washington Territory
8th May 1854

Andrew Murray, Esq.,
7 Nelson Street,
Edinburgh

Dear Sir,

In reply to your favour of 9th February – received some days ago – I regret to mention that I am unable to give you any information regarding the packet of seeds, which you anticipated would be sent by Mr Jeffrey from this place to York Factory, and thence to London by one of the Hudson's Bay Company's vessels. No person in this establishment is aware of Mr Jeffrey having left such a package, about which I have just made the most rigid enquiry.

The Box mentioned in mine of last of December as having been forwarded to Vancouver Island to go from thence to London arrived there too late for the ship of the season, but you may depend on it being shipped by the first vessel which sails.

I am, dear Sir,
Your obedient Servant,
Peter Skene Ogden

Journal: Fort Yuma, 4 May 1854

In the saloon last evening, I struck up a conversation with two soldiers who were regaling those around with a tale of derring-do featuring Kit Carsen. By their account he was (or is) a living man, not only a work of fiction on the page. He fought his first battle on the Upper Gila River, against the Apache Indians when they attacked his expedition. I kept my tongue, but only with the greatest of efforts.

I have secured all I need for my onward journey – the mule of all things proving most troublesome – and I leave before dawn tomorrow. I wrote a short letter to McKinlay, Garrioch & Co. while I was in San Diego, concerning future transportation requirements for a box of specimens, thinking I might be at this place for more months yet, but it will matter little to them that my plans have changed. I have found no appetite for communicating with the committee, and can only hope that they will approve of my intention to explore a new territory on their behalf. In expectation of a communication from them, given the formal completion of my contract at the end of last year, I have left word with Adams & Co. that any letters can be held for me at San Diego.

Email: Arnold Arboretum, Boston, 1 April, present day

From: helen@arnoldarboretum.org

Hi Ben,

Here's a scan of the letter I mentioned. Also, I found a second notice in the paper, three months after the first – also attached. This one doesn't pull any punches.

I can't tell you how excited I am about the exhibition and

the possibility of a job here. Thank you so much (and fingers crossed for the funding)! H.

Letter: William Murray to Andrew Murray †

William Murray
131 Montgomery Street
San Francisco
19th May 1854

Dear Andrew,

I yesterday received your letter enclosing one to Jeffrey and one for Mr Ogden, and with instructions to recall the former and stop his credits.

I went again to McKinlay, Garrioch & Co., and they have deciphered his address to be Fort Yuma on the Gila River (just where it joins the Colorado), where he says he will probably be until 1st August, and directs his letters to be forwarded by Adams & Co.'s Express to the care of their Agent at San Diego, Mr F. Ames.

I accordingly put his letter in an envelope addressed in conformity with these instructions and took it to Adams & Co.'s Express and told them (as they are Bankers as well as Express men) that the letter contained his recall, and at the same time called their attention to the advertisement which I have caused to be put in the *Alta California* and which is:-

The Oregon Association hereby notify that JOHN JEFFREY, Botanical Collector, is no longer in their service, and that they will not be liable for any debts he may contract.

By order of the Committee,

For Andrew MURRAY, secretary,

W. MURRAY, 131 Montgomery Street.

I also called the attention of Page, Bacon & Co., who I was told had cashed his drafts, to the advertisement, without comment. The same with Davidson (Rothschild's agent) and I told McKinlay, Garrioch & Co. of his recall.

I am inclined to think from their description of the man that he is honest. They say he is a hard-working, enthusiastic, very steady and temperate man, and that just before starting for San Diego he was some three weeks arranging the proceeds of his excursions; they doubt not that he despatched them. He had been for some weeks sick before that, which accounts for part of the long stay in San Francisco.

I think he has misapprehended the nature of his mission, and supposes that a single specimen also of everything he saw was all that was required of him, fancying rather that he was sent to find out what was here, than that he was required to stock H. B. Majesty's Islands with it.

I met the Consul just now and he said he had received another letter to Jeffrey. I forwarded it along with yours. The Consul says that he never called at the Consulate, that there have been quite a budget of letters and other things there for him; which has since been forwarded to him by McKinlay, Garrioch & Co. the same time as your previous letters went.

I hardly expect to see him back, and I hope he may be able to show you on his arrival home that he is only an ass.

Among other things which he neglected to tell you of, he informed McKinlay, Garrioch & Co. that he could do nothing on Vancouver Island on account of the brush-wood which is so thick as to be impenetrable except by cutting your way axe in hand, information which I quietly put into our own pipe for private smoking. Another thing – that he intended to come out here again – so we must 'hurry up the cakes', although he will not be a formidable competitor.

The letter from Mr Ogden I took to the Office of Allan,

Lowe & Co. the correspondents of the Hudson's Bay Company in San Francisco, and they have promised to forward it. A young Scotchman there told me that he knew Mr Jeffrey very well and intended to have called on me on sight of the advertisement, to inquire what it meant, as he believed him incapable of doing anything wrong, but said he was slow and very quiet. I gave as the reason that the Society was about to be dissolved.

You will probably think that I ought to have been able to find out Jeffrey when he was here, but at that time, I neither knew that McKinlay, Garrioch & Co. were acquainted with him, nor that Allan, Lowe & Co. were connected with the Hudson's Bay Company.

Now then – I have done all you told me to do, and for the result you must 'let her rip'.

I spoke to Sam Price about it and he says the only satisfaction you can get out of a fellow of that kind is to come out here and shoot him through the navel with a Mississippi Yaeger, nobody will say anything to you; or if there is an investigation it will be brought in justifiable homicide.

There was an advertisement in one of the papers the other day, somewhat part of this fashion –

'The publication of the Police Gazette will be postponed for a month in consequence of the assassination of the Editor.'

Them's not the words, but them's the sentiments. Cool, isn't it?

I remain,
Your affectionate brother,
William Murray

GREEN GOLD

ALTA CALIFORNIA

Advertisement: *Daily Alta California*, **22 May 1854** †

CITY HAT STORE — ADAMS & WHITE, 143 Commercial Street, opposite the Mint, will introduce THIS DAY a new style of HAT, particularly adapted to young men. Call and see them.

ADAMS & WHITE

THE OREGON BOTANICAL ASSOCIATION, hereby notify that JOHN JEFFREY, Botanical Collector, is no longer in their service, and that they will not be liable for any debts he may contract.

By order of the Committee,
For ANDW. MURRAY, secretary, W. MURRAY, 131
Montgomery Street.

CITY WARRANTS FOR SALE—In sums to suit, all in order, and will be received by the city in payment of the third instalment of the city slip property due on the 29th inst.

C. H. WEST, Stock & Money Broker, 157 Montgomery
Street, near Burgoyne's Bank.

Journal: A little life, 29 May 1854

My little Kapka is one year old today.
  In my own mind, I am always with you, My Darling girl.
  May the Lord bless you and protect you.

Letter: James Veitch to Andrew Murray †

Nursery,
Exeter
24th June 1854

Mr Andrew Murray
Edinburgh

Dear Sir,
  I am obliged by your letter offering the Californian bulbs which are not the sort of things to suit us here.
  I forwarded your letter to my son in London (the Exotic Nursery, Chelsea) in case he might wish for any of them, and if so you will at once hear from him.
  I can give you very little information respecting Jeffrey. Our Mr Lobb fell in with him once I think in Vancouver Land and they were together a day or two. The only remark I recollect Mr Lobb making was that from the heavy expenses in that Country he did not think the Funds at Mr Jeffrey's disposal were sufficient to make large collections, the expenses being so heavy for taking things across to the coast for shipment. The things we have raised from his seeds have been very few but I conclude we have neighbour's fare and must therefore be content.
  I am, Dear Sir,
  Yours truly,
  James Veitch

Letter: HBC to Andrew Murray †

Hudson's Bay House
London
28th July 1854

Andrew Murray, Esq.,
Edinburgh

Sir,

With reference to my letter of 27th March, I am directed by the Governor and Committee of the Hudson's Bay Company to acquaint you that advices have been received from their agents at Fort Vancouver, Oregon Territory, stating that an advance of Five Hundred Dollars has been made to Mr John Jeffrey at that place on the 6th April 1853 which is still outstanding against your society. The amount at an exchange of 4/2 per dollar is £104.3.4.

I am, Sir,
Your obedient servant,
W. G. Smith
Assistant Secretary

Journal: Upper Gila River, 1 August 1854

33° 5' 3" N

No more, dear God, no more. I am ending this decomposition. By this act, I will find a new beginning. My own genesis.

SAPROGENESIS

LIFE FROM DEATH

Letter: Oregon Botanical Association to the
Subscribers †

OREGON BOTANICAL ASSOCIATION

> 7 Nelson Street,
> Edinburgh
> 10th January 1857

Dear Sir,

The Committee of the Association had formerly occasion to explain to the Contributors the painful position in which they were placed by the absence of communications from their Collector, Mr Jeffrey.

In the earlier part of his career Mr Jeffrey had proved his possession of the qualities befitting a Botanical Collector, a fact which made his desertion of duty only the more to be regretted.

Though the success of the Association, in the fulfilment of its original purpose, has fallen greatly short of what they had every reason to hope for, and at one time to anticipate; it has yet unquestionably been instrumental in introducing several new specimens of hardy Trees, Shrubs, &c., of great beauty and interest, and some of the former they confidently believe will prove to be of great value.

I am,
Sir,
Your most obedient Servant,
Andrew Murray, Secretary

Article by Andrew Murray, 1860 †

Some subscribers to the Association, remembering totally that the third and last year of Jeffrey's engagement terminated unsuccessfully, and that they had just reason to be seen dissatisfied with his conduct during that year, sometimes speak of his expedition as a failure. But it is unjust so to term it; and if they would only remember the quantities of novelties which were discovered and introduced through his means, they would rather treat it as a great success, which only assumes the aspect of a partial failure from the knowledge that, great as it was, it ought to have been, and might have been, greater still. No one could have worked more conscientiously and more perseveringly than Jeffrey did during that first two years of his employment, and bearing in mind that Menzies and Douglas went to virgin country, his collections do him credit, even as compared with theirs.

From: Johnstone, J. T. (1939). John Jeffrey and the Oregon Expedition, Notes from the Royal Botanic Garden, Edinburgh, 20: 14.

Memory of James Anderson, 1925 †

Few living people possibly remember to have met Jeffrey, the naturalist, after whom many native plants are named. Mr Jeffrey reached Fort Victoria in 1851 having come through Fort Colville where my father was stationed, and I was therefore the chosen companion of Mr Jeffrey in his nearby excursions. A woodpecker slain by Mr Jeffrey in the edge of the woods where the city nursery now stands remains impressed on my memory. I never heard anything further of Mr Jeffrey after his departure until 1911, when visiting the Royal Botanic Gardens in Edinburgh and conversing with the director, Professor Isaac Balfour [son of Professor John Balfour], the name of Mr Jeffrey came up. I was then informed by Professor Balfour that after leaving Fort Victoria he found his way to San Francisco, then in the throes of the gold excitements, and was never heard of afterwards, probably murdered by the lawless ruffians who congregate at all mining centres. Naturally Professor Balfour was greatly interested in meeting someone who actually had seen Mr Jeffrey.

From: Anderson, J. R. (1925). Trees and Shrubs: Food, Medicinal, and Poisonous Plants of British Columbia. British Columbia Department of Education.

ECOLOGUE

Tulelake, California, 24 June, present day

Emily glanced at the clock again before looking over to the old box on the sideboard, her eyes drifting over its thick leather strap and the familiar knots in its wooden sides. *She'll be here at any moment; better put some coffee on.* Reaching for her stick, she started to rise awkwardly from the deep armchair.

The doorbell rang, making her start. She missed Biz when anyone came to the door; her excited bark used to provide a welcome sense of security. She opened the door to find a smartly dressed young woman standing on the step, clutching a simple bouquet.

'Hello, Mrs Edwards? I'm Helen, the researcher from the Arboretum.'

'Of course you are. Sorry to keep you waiting – it takes me a while to reach the door these days.'

'I brought these for you, Mrs Edwards,' said Helen, passing her the flowers and shouldering her bag.

'How delightful. Thank you. Please call me Emily. Come on in.'

Helen entered the condo, taking in the variety of fine antique furniture that filled every corner of the small front room. Weaving slowly between tables and chairs, she followed the old woman as she shuffled towards the back room, waiting patiently as she manoeuvred herself into a large pillowed chair. It offered a fine view over an overgrown back yard, and between the neighbouring houses a ridge of hills was just visible in the distance.

'Oh, look now, I meant to put some coffee on. Let me see—'

'Honestly Mrs Edwards… Emily. I picked one up on the way over. Can I get you something?'

'No, I'm fine, thank you.' Emily gestured to an armchair next to her. 'Have a seat, please.'

Helen settled in the comfy chair next to the window.

266

Family photos crowded the window sill, featuring several happy generations. Most of them had been captured in the outdoors, on the lakeside or a trail in the woods. A formation of geese flew over the garden, heading for the lake.

'Now, tell me what all this is about,' said Emily. 'Your call came out of the blue, and you didn't tell me that much. I've been thinking it must be important for you to travel all this way.'

Helen felt the intensity of the old woman's stare, and it put her a little on edge. 'So, it's—'

'And, like I told you on the phone,' interrupted Emily, barely pausing for breath, 'I'm pleased you could come, as I have a few heirlooms here which I think might be of interest.'

'Sure. I'd like to show you this first,' said Helen, reaching into her bag to remove a small book. Its brown leather cover was deeply stained and creased, and a long lace held it closed. 'This is only one of the six journals,' she said, stroking its cover with her fingertips before passing it on. 'I brought this one as it's the last in the series, and also because it contained a letter, tucked inside the back cover.'

'Yes, I see, but exactly how— Oh my, look at the writing! It's very old.' Emily turned to the small table between them to reach for her reading glasses. 'May I see…?'

Helen watched Emily's face intently as she read, feeling excited for the old woman. She waited patiently, allowing her time to decipher the thin looped handwriting. More birds flew over, this time a dozen white egrets.

Finally, Helen asked, 'What's in the passage you're reading?'

'It's written by a man, all about his baby daughter, and there's mention of California too,' said Emily. 'The date at the top of the entry is 1854.'

Helen settled into her chair a little. 'I think I should start at the beginning. Shall I…?'

'Why, yes,' said Emily, leaning back with a sigh. 'I'm still rather puzzled by quite how this is connected to me, and why you've come all this way.'

'It was last September, and the first day of my six-month internship, when I was given a menial task of sorting through some miscellaneous materials in the archives at the Arboretum. To be honest, it was a stroke of luck, really. Anyway, I came across a bundle of these old journals and decided to peek inside.'

Emily looked intently at Helen, returning her reading glasses to the table but keeping hold of the journal. 'Go on.'

'When I told Ben – I mean the professor – about the journals, he wanted to see for himself. He became more interested than I expected, but it wasn't until I showed him the loose letter that he got really excited.' Helen paused for effect, enjoying telling the story to such an eager listener.

'So, who was this man, and why did his journals end up at your institution?'

'His name was John Jeffrey. He was a Scottish explorer and botanist who came to Oregon, Washington and California to hunt for plants to be introduced to Britain. His journals reached us soon after the Arboretum was established.'

'And what has this got to do with me?'

Helen found it hard to contain her excitement, feeling an unfamiliar lump rise in her throat. She coughed. 'The professor was very pleased by the discovery, and decided that I should focus my whole internship researching everything connected with this man, John Jeffrey. We wanted to understand exactly why his journals were in our archives, especially when we realised, early on, that he had been sponsored by a botanic garden in Scotland. It turns out that the people in Scotland never knew for sure that these journals even existed.'

'Just think, for all those years, they must have wondered what became of them. Sorry, I interrupted you…'

'It was only when I read the last couple of journals – including this one – that I realised John Jeffrey had started a family here in America, and never returned to Scotland. This got me thinking—'

'Yes—'

'Well, maybe he had some descendants. Maybe I could track them down,' said Helen, watching the realisation dawn across Emily's wrinkled face.

'Oh my goodness, is that why you are here? Seriously!'

'Yes – yes, it is.' Helen was powerless to prevent a huge grin from spreading across her face. 'You see, I believe that you're a direct descendant of John Jeffrey: in fact, his great-great-granddaughter.'

'That's incredible. I can't believe it!'

'I know, right. If you can handle a little more excitement, I've been asked to invite you and your family to a special exhibition to be held at the Arboretum next year. I've just been appointed as the curator, you see, and I'll be working full-time on this for the next two years, now that we've got major funding. The professor from Scotland is coming over – they have an unusual name for them over there, the "Regius Keeper" – to give a lecture. We'll have some of John Jeffrey's original letters and botanical specimens brought over from Scotland, and of course these journals, and we'll put them all on display together. We'll also have the original minute book of the committee that managed the expedition. We're talking about commissioning some botanical paintings of his most important discoveries. We've found this wonderful Scottish artist who has—'

'I see, well, I mean, this is all so exciting. It's a quite a long way for me to travel, but... perhaps my daughter could accompany me.' Emily paused, absentmindedly bringing the journal up to her lips, deep in thought. 'I mean, I would love to come if I can.'

'We'll do whatever we can to make it possible for you. After all, Emily, you will be our guest of honour!'

'Oh, my goodness!'

'One more thing. We've also managed to track down a direct descendant of Alexander Caulfield Anderson, who was a close companion of John Jeffrey. Her name's Nancy, and she's been researching the Hudson's Bay Company and the York Factory Express for the last few years. She's even written a couple of books. She's looking forward to meeting you; it will be quite some reunion!'

'I just can't believe it. It's so much to take in.' Emily straightened up suddenly. 'Look, I'm forgetting things, I've got a surprise for you.' She pointed to the box sitting on a long sideboard. 'Would you mind? Be careful, it's heavier than it looks.'

Helen carried the wooden box to Emily's side.

'I'm only beginning to realise as we talk that there could be more to this than I thought. You see, I tried to find out more information about these things, but I didn't get very far.' Emily started to unbuckle the leather strap holding closed its curved lid. 'My grandson showed a few artefacts at his school recently and a teacher suggested we should have them valued. But I'm not interested in that. I think they have more value to a family than merely money, don't you?'

'I can't wait to see what's in there!'

'Yes, well, this box and all its contents have been passed down between us women in the family. There's nothing written down to say it must be done this way – it just seems the right thing to do.'

'Can I see?' asked Helen.

'Yes, of course. Just lift that latch to open it.'

'This is so beautiful!' Helen exclaimed, picking up an ornately decorated horn, her wonder turning to surprise when something rattled inside.

'That is one thing that I do know something about. It's a purse made by the Klamath, the Native American tribe that lived in this part of northern California.' Emily reached out a hand. 'Pass it to me, would you, and I'll show you something else.' She tipped its contents carefully into her hand and a number of small white shells, shaped like miniature tusks, tumbled out. Each was delicately engraved and had a small hole drilled at one end.

'I know what these are!' Helen said, unable to hide her excitement, then looking again into the box, taking in its other items. 'Oh my! There are some really old instruments here. Isn't this a type of sextant? But look, there's a dip pen. It could be the one that John Jeffrey wrote with!'

They sat in silence for a while, both absorbed by their own discoveries.

'I've still not shown you the letter,' Helen said, picking up the old journal. She carefully slid the folded sheets of paper from their resting place. 'I'll let you read it in peace for a moment.'

Letter: John Jeffrey to Charles Sargent

3rd December 1873

Charles Sprague Sargent Esq.
Dwight House
Brookline Estate
Massachusetts

Sir,

IN STRICTEST CONFIDENCE

I understand you have been appointed recently as the founding director of a new arboretum, following the generous gift of land by Mr James Arnold. It pleases me greatly that your plans will ensure that it will not only provide a pleasure ground for the citizens of America, but also an encyclopaedic tree museum for scientists allied to the university.

I was in New Mexico in the summer of 1854, some 200 miles upstream of Fort Yuma (33° 5' 3" N), with 400 miles remaining before I reached what I believed to be my goal, when I had an epiphany. My path had been fixed to following a fading emerald thread, perilously entwined with the meandering water, while beyond beckoned a treeless barren landscape: devoid of beauty, holding no joy, promising no future. All that I lived for, and all that I loved, I had abandoned and left behind: my beautiful baby daughter Kapka, the bountiful forests, a life at one with nature. I realised then that I could restore the fabric of my life by simply turning around.

You will no doubt be wondering why I am sharing this with you. There is little reason why you should know much of me or my exploits, and you will be curious, I am sure, as to why a stranger should send you a box containing a bundle of journals. I hope you will allow me to explain in

272

some detail the background, and the reasons for me writing to you without so much as an introduction.

Some 20 years ago, I was employed by the Royal Botanic Garden Edinburgh to conduct an expedition to Oregon Country and beyond, searching for botanical specimens. The results of my efforts were intended to promote diversity among the *Coniferae* of Britain, among other plants and even insects, but in no small way also to line the pockets of a large number of subscribers, including among them some of the wealthiest gentlemen in that country and some commercial horticultural nurseries.

I was despatched in 1850, being then an extremely 'green' young man and, were it not for the support of many within the Hudson's Bay Company, the inadequate logistics and finances from my sponsors could easily have led to utter failure on my part. After crossing the continent, I undertook botanical collecting throughout much of Oregon, Washington and California, sending back 10 full boxes of labelled specimens and seeds, many of which I believe to have been entirely new to botany, and naturally of some considerable financial worth to the subscribers in Britain. I have since kept a passing interest in the fruits of my labours and have been gratified to learn that a number of species bear my name, including *Dodecatheon jeffreyi*, *Penstemon jeffreyanus* and *Pinus jeffreyi*.

I fulfilled the full part of my three-year contract, resisting in any significant way the many temptations during this time that may otherwise have lured me away from botany. I wrote letters to my employer and provided detailed labels to accompany the specimens collected, including their latitude, altitude and soil, not to mention a description of the plants and their principal features. These will have provided those at home with a clear picture of my location and exploits, and of my achievements.

There is only one part of my contract that I failed to comply with, and for which my employer will have been justifiably dissatisfied. This was the keeping of journals to record my exploits, discoveries and the territories explored. Yet I did, in fact, keep a record and more than likely wrote about my experiences in greater depth than any person might reasonably have expected. Where I will be seen to have failed is in not passing these on to my employer.

Your first and principal question will undoubtedly be to ask me why I did not share these journals. I have asked myself the same on many occasions, yet even today, on rereading a few of the entries, I am reminded of the significant personal value that they had to me. I was fortunate to meet many generous and gifted people during my travels, yet fulfilling my duty was a lonely experience, and it was only through writing that I was able to keep the flame alight for my real purpose in coming to this country. Amid the rush for gold, let alone the sometimes brutal struggle for survival, there was little appreciation for my botanical mission.

There is a second reason, beyond the act of writing in support of my expedition, and this reasoning may appear foolish to anyone but myself. Simply, the journals became my friend and confidant. I found, almost from the very first entry, that I relished the moment when I put my pen to paper, of pondering how best to share my experiences, and later, as time went on, the pleasure of reading them again. Over time, I became more honest and less guarded in the details I chronicled, to the point when, even if I had found the strength to part company with them, their contents were quite unsuitable for my employer or any other living soul that might know me.

I have pondered for considerable time the best course of action concerning these journals, even contemplating on a number of occasions their destruction. Yet I realised that in the future, someone with a little interest in history may find some of their content informative, if not a little revealing as to the nature of those times. I also hope that those with a fascination for botany may discover details of interest, especially allied to records received by the Royal Botanic Garden Edinburgh.

I have been blessed in love, having once had a devoted wife, and I have raised a beautiful daughter whom I foolishly lost, before having the sense to recover her. Recently, I celebrated the arrival of a granddaughter. Our family home is among the nature that I love, while my journals now belong to a previous life and I no longer have need of them. My decision is that they should be stored under lock and key, to remain private for the remainder of my lifetime. I believe the archives of what will surely become a prestigious arboretum would be the ideal home for them. In time, I hope that some person may be inclined to distribute them, perhaps to the Garden in Edinburgh.

I therefore trust you personally to be the archivist of my journals in adherence with my wishes stated above, their storage to be confined within the new library that I know you are compiling. You will notice that I offer no return address, as it is my preference not to enter into any correspondence, nor will I become a revenant. I am truly indebted to you, Sir.

Only when we truly value nature will we lay the foundations for future profit. I am confident that this is a sentiment about which we will be in accord.

Yours sincerely,
John Jeffrey

Gold to Green

Two dead strode through the sunlit glade;
Soft snow yielding under tamarack shoes.
Law unto Lavoisier alone,
Dazzling life from gold to green.

APPENDIX

Botanical Notes

BOTANICAL ACHIEVEMENTS

John Jeffrey collected at least 400 plant specimens and the seeds of 199 species. His collection included 35 conifer tree species, his main purpose, including: eleven pine (*Pinus*); four species and a variety of fir (*Abies*); four spruce (*Picea*); five juniper (*Juniperus*); three hemlock (*Tsuga*); two false cedar (*Chamaecyparis*); and one each of cypress (*Cupressus*), larch (*Larix*), Douglas-fir (*Pseudotsuga*), yew (*Taxus*) and red cedar (*Thuya*).

A helpful summary of his conifer collections is provided by:

Woods, P. and Woods, J. (2003). The Oregon Expedition 1850–1854: John Jeffrey and his Conifers. Acta Horticulturae, 615, 289–295. DOI: 10.17660/ ActaHortic.2003.615.30

BOTANICAL NAMES

The names given to plants often vary over time. Taxonomists first classified them according to their appearance and similarity to other plants – often disagreeing with one another – while more recently they have been arranged following genetic studies using their DNA. Scientific names consist of two parts, the genus and species; an example being *Pinus jeffreyi*, where *Pinus* identifies the pine genus, and *jeffreyi* the species name. Often, John Jeffrey was unsure of the species name, in which case he might simply have written *Pinus* Sp., meaning an unknown species of pine.

There was a great deal of confusion in the 19th century when it came to classifying conifers, with plants often placed in different genera (plural of genus) by different taxonomists. Jeffrey referred to some conifers as *Abies* (firs), but we now classify many of them as *Picea* (spruce). He also referred to the Douglas–fir under two different genera! Such confusion is evident in Professor Balfour's letter to Andrew Murray on 6th June 1855:

> There are some errors in the names. *Nobilis* and *grandis* should commence with small letters. Why call one a *Picea* and the other a *Pinus*? Either take *Pinus* for all and make the other sub-genera, or restrict *Pinus* to those with leaves in twos, threes, fours, fives, or sixes and give the name *Abies, Picea, Pinus* &c. to the others.

It was the convention in the 19th century to write the Latin species name using a capital letter when it was a proper noun (e.g. *Primula Scotica*), but today it will always begin with a lower case (i.e. *Primula scotica*).

The following table lists some of the principal species featured in *Green Gold* which have since been altered. Both archaic and modern scientific names are provided, along with the most used modern common name, with the collection number (if known).

Scientific archaic	Common modern	Scientific modern	Collection no.	Notes
Abies alba	white spruce	*Picea glauca*	—	Archaic name should not be confused with the same modern scientific name used for European silver fir. See also *Abies Canadensis*.
Abies Canadensis	white spruce	*Picea glauca*	—	Mentioned in description of *Abies Pattoniana*.
Abies Douglasii	Douglas-fir	*Pseudotsuga menziesii*	—	Also named by Jeffrey as *Pinus Douglasii* (see below).
Abies grandis	grand fir	*Abies grandis*	393	Collected September 1851.
Abies magnifica	California red fir	*Abies magnifica*	1480	A specimen from Box No. 10 had grown to 11 ft. tall in 1872.
Abies Menziesii	Sitka spruce	*Picea sitchensis*	—	No specimen provided. 52 cones sent.
Abies Pattoniana	mountain hemlock	*Tsuga mertensiana*	430	
Abies rubra	black spruce	*Picea mariana*	—	Collected near Oxford House. Originally misidentified as *Picea rubens* (eastern or red spruce).

Abies taxifolia	western hemlock	*Tsuga heterophylla*	—	Discovered 24 April 1852. Sufficient seed collected to satisfy all the subscribers. Became an important forest species in Britain.
Amelanchier alnifolia	saskatoon	*Amelanchier alnifolia*	—	An ingredient of pemmican.
Cupressus Macnabiana	Macnab cypress	*Cupressus macnabiana*	1481	
Dodecatheon Jeffreyi	Jeffrey's shooting star	*Dodecatheon jeffreyi*	601	Collected 20 September 1852. Later named in Jeffrey's honour.
Juglandaceae Sp.	California black walnut	*Juglans californica*	1489	Collected 20 November 1853, Bay of San Francisco.
Juniperus Californica	California juniper	*Juniperus californica*	1475	
Larix Americana	tamarack	*Larix laricina*	—	Collected 13 August 1850.
Lewisia rediviva	bitterroot	*Lewisia rediviva*	32	Collected 16 June 1851. Extraordinarily, 14 months after their receipt it was noted that some roots were still green in the herbarium, and were successfully propagated. A flowering specimen was later exhibited.

Penstemon jeffreyanus	azure penstemon	*Penstemon azureus*	1116	Now renamed, but in its original form recognised Jeffrey as collector.
Picea Lasiocarpa	Pacific silver fir	*Abies amabilis*	409	
Pinus albicaulis	whitebark pine	*Pinus albicaulis*	398	Seeds stolen by the Nutcracker! Originally misidentified as *Pinus flexilis*.
Pinus Balfouriana	foxtail pine	*Pinus balfouriana*	618	New species discovered by Jeffrey in September 1852. Sent in Box No. 5.
Pinus douglasii	Douglas-fir	*Pseudotsuga menziesii*	—	Also named by Jeffrey as *Abies Douglasii*.
Pinus Jeffreyi	Jeffrey pine	*Pinus jeffreyi*	731	Named in Jeffrey's honour.
Pinus lambertiana	sugar pine	*Pinus lambertiana*	612	Seeds stolen by a ground rat.
Pinus monticola	western white pine	*Pinus monticola*	706	
Pinus Murrayana	Sierra lodgepole pine	*Pinus contorta* subsp. *murrayana*	740	Box No. 5, received April 1853.
Pinus Sp.	lodgepole pine	*Pinus contorta*	753	Collected near Mount Jefferson, December 1852. Sent in Box No. 6, February 1853.

Thuja craigana	incense cedar	*Calocedrus decurrens*	—	First discovered by John Fremont in 1846, but the first seeds were collected by Jeffrey and sent to Britain.

Outmoded Terms

Outmoded term	Modern term
buffalo	American bison (*Bison bison*)
Columbia	A district in the British Territories of the Pacific Northwest, adjacent to Rupert's Land. Also known as the Columbia Department, controlled by the Hudson's Bay Company.
Indian	Native American
Métis	Of mixed race, usually referring to those from Native American and white colonist parentage. Also known as a 'half-blood'.
Rupert's Land	Previously one of the British Territories of mainland North America, comprising the fur-trading area under control of the Hudson's Bay Company. Mostly now Canada, plus small areas within four US states.

Historical fiction, through the voice of a first-person narrator, inevitably involves language that has become outdated. Certain terms have not only become unfashionable or proven inaccurate, but are considered offensive. Such terms have been adopted only to ensure historical accuracy, and are not intended to cause offence to contemporary readers. Some outmoded geographical territories are also described.

Archival Materials †

The majority of archival materials cited in *Green Gold* were accessed from the library of the Royal Botanic Garden Edinburgh. Exceptions were the 1852 articles in the *Gardeners' Chronicle*, the entry in the *Journal of Occurrences* of Fort Nisqually the same year, the two notices during 1854 in the newspaper *Daily Alta California*, plus the extracts of articles published in 1860, 1872 and 1925.

Minutes of OBA, Royal Botanic Garden Edinburgh,
    22 November 1849
Letter to Professor Balfour, 5 December 1849
Letter to Professor Balfour, 4 February 1850
Minutes of OBA, 6 February 1850
Minutes of OBA Sub-Committee, 20 February 1850
Minutes of OBA Sub-Committee, 23 February 1850
Letter to Professor Balfour, 25 February 1850
Minutes of OBA Sub-Committee, 28 February 1850
Minutes of OBA, 20 March 1850
Letter to Oregon Botanical Association
Detailed Instruction to the Collector, Oregon Expedition
Minute of Agreement between the Association for

procuring seeds from Oregon and John Jeffrey,
24 May 1850
Letter to Andrew Murray, 3 June 1850
Letter to Professor Balfour, 8 June 1850
Letter to Professor Balfour, June 11 1850
Letter to Professor Balfour, 1 July 1850
Letter to Professor Balfour, 20 August 1850
Letter to OBA Subscribers, 20 November 1850
Letter to John Balfour, 7 April 1851
Minutes of OBA, 29 September 1851
Minutes of OBA, 6 November 1851
Letter to Andrew Murray, 17 November 1851
Journal of Occurrences, 18 June 1852
Letter from Post Office, 23 August 1852
Minutes of OBA, 24 August 1852
Scotch expedition to Oregon, *Gardeners' Chronicle*,
28 August 1852
Letter to Dr Greville, 31 August 1852
Letter to Subscribers, 4 September 1852
Letter to Subscribers, 4 September 1852
Letter to Professor Balfour, 18 September 1852
Garden Memoranda, *Gardeners' Chronicle*, 2 October 1852
Letter to Andrew Murray, 5 November 1852
Minutes of OBA, 12 January 1853
Note with Package No. 5, 22 January 1853
Letter to John Balfour, 15 February 1853
Letter to Professor Balfour, 14 March 1853
Minutes of OBA, 14 April 1853
Letter to John Jeffrey, 15 April 1853
Letter to Subscribers, 16 April 1853
Letter to Andrew Murray, 9 June 1853
Letter to Subscribers, 18 June 1853
Minutes of OBA, 1 July 1853
Letter to Andrew Murray, 13 October 1853
Letter to Andrew Murray, 18 October 1853
Minutes of OBA, 23 November 1853
Letter to Andrew Murray, 7 December 1853

Letter to Andrew Murray, 5 January 1854
Letter to Andrew Murray, 25 January 1854
Letter to Andrew Murray, 25 January 1854
Letter to Andrew Murray, 1 February 1854
Daily Alta California, 4 February 1854
Minutes of OBA, 23 March 1854
Letter to Subscribers, 24 March 1854
Letter to Andrew Murray, 27 March 1854
Letter to Professor Balfour, 29 March 1854
Letter to Andrew Murray, 8 May 1854
Letter to Andrew Murray, 19 May 1854
Daily Alta California, 22 May 1854
Letter to Andrew Murray, 24 June 1854
Letter to Andrew Murray, 28 July 1854
Letter to Subscribers, 10 January 1857
Article by Andrew Murray, 1860
Extract from an article by Alexander Caulfield Anderson, 1872
Memory of James Anderson, 1925

Biographies

The following short biographies describe the main cast of real-life historical characters which feature in *Green Gold*.

John Jeffrey (14 November 1826 – unknown) was born at Forneth, Perthshire in Scotland, the eldest son of John and Helen Jeffrey. The family moved to Fife and in 1841 lived in Lochore, where 15-year-old John became a servant or agricultural worker at East Blair House a few miles away. In January 1849, the Royal Botanic Garden Edinburgh employed 23-year-old Jeffrey as a gardener. He made a name for himself there and reportedly came to the attention of **James McNab**, curator of the garden. Energetic and knowledgeable about botany, Jeffrey won a prize for the best dried-plant collection made from the vicinity of Edinburgh. In 1850, he was appointed collector to the Oregon Botanical Association by **John Balfour**, and the same year, aged 23 and a half years, Jeffrey left for the continent of North America. He sailed, walked and paddled some 10,000 miles through the British Territories and the states of Oregon, Washington and California, collecting botanical specimens. Thanks to his work, the seeds from 119 species and more than 400 plant specimens were collected and sent to the Herbarium at the Royal Botanic Garden

Edinburgh, including those of 35 conifer species. Two plant species still bear his name, *Dodecatheon jeffreyi* and *Pinus jeffreyi*, while a third, *Penstemon jeffreyanus*, was later renamed by botanists. He is also remembered by Mount Jeffrey near Victoria on Vancouver Island, and by Jeffrey Peak in the Fraser Valley of British Columbia. John Jeffrey was last seen in San Francisco in 1854, thought to be heading next to New Mexico.

Professor John Hutton Balfour (15 September 1808 – 11 February 1884) was appointed professor of botany at Edinburgh University in 1845, where he was a popular lecturer, and nicknamed 'Woody Fibre'. At the same time he was elected Regius Keeper at the Royal Botanic Garden Edinburgh (RBGE) where he served until his death. His appointment only came after a bitter contest with Joseph Dalton Hooker, a close friend of Charles Darwin and second son of **William Jackson Hooker**. John Balfour was elected chairman of the Oregon Botanical Association. His son, Sir Isaac Bayley Balfour, succeeded his father as Regius Keeper of RBGE, and cared for Oregon Expedition matters for years afterwards, eventually meeting **Alexander Caulfield Anderson** in 1911. The rare pine *Pinus balfouriana*, discovered by **John Jeffrey**, takes his name.

Andrew Dickson Murray (19 February 1812 – 10 January 1878) was a Scottish lawyer, botanist, zoologist and entomologist. In botany, he specialised in the *Coniferae*. He was secretary to the Oregon Botanical Association. His brother William Murray lived in North America and they corresponded regularly about **John Jeffrey**, notably during 1854. William's letter to his brother in May of that year was barred from publication by **John Balfour** until after both brothers had died, presumably to protect their reputation and that of the Garden. During the 1860s, Andrew Murray corresponded regularly with Charles Darwin.

Sir William Gibson-Craig (2 August 1797 – 12 March 1878), was a Scottish advocate and politician. He was a Member of Parliament for Edinburgh, and a Junior Lord of the Treasury in Lord John Russell's government from 1846 to 1852. He corresponded with Andrew Murray concerning financial matters of the Oregon Botanical Association. He met John Jeffrey in London shortly before he left for North America.

James McNab (25 April 1810 – 19 November 1878) was born in Surrey, England, but his family moved to Scotland when his father William was appointed curator of the Royal Botanic Garden Edinburgh. In 1834, he travelled with Robert Brown to explore North America. In 1849 he succeeded his father in becoming curator of the Royal Botanic Garden Edinburgh under Regius Keeper **John Balfour**. He attended many of the meetings of the Oregon Botanical Association, acting as co-secretary.

John Lindley (5 February 1799 – 1 November 1865) was an English botanist and gardener. John Jeffrey met him shortly before departing for North America, while he was chair of botany, University College of London. Along with **Sir William Hooker**, he was sent most of Jeffrey's plant specimens to identify and classify.

Sir William Jackson Hooker (6 July 1785 – 12 August 1865) was raised by a relatively wealthy family and funded his first botanical expedition himself, visiting Iceland. In 1820, he was appointed Regius Professor at the University of Glasgow, where he supported the creation of the Botanic Garden. He later convinced successive British governments that botanists should be included in expeditions. In 1841, he was appointed director of the Royal Botanic Gardens at Kew, London. In 1845, his son Joseph applied to be chair of botany at University of Edinburgh – which traditionally included the role of Regius Keeper at the Royal Botanic

Garden Edinburgh – but was beaten to the post by local botanist **John Balfour**, much to the surprise of **W. J.** Hooker's friend Charles Darwin. He was recognised during his lifetime as an outstanding botanist and was sent (along with **John Lindley**) many of Jeffrey's specimens to identify and classify. His relationship with Balfour and the Oregon Botanical Association appeared fractious; **John Jeffrey** met him in June 1850, finding him critical of the planned expedition. Later he frequently questioned the quality of the specimens forwarded to him for identification, and published an article openly criticising some names tentatively given in a list meant to be a private communication. Some botanists have suggested his naming of *Penstemon jeffreyanus* was an intellectual insult to the collector.

William Lobb (6 July 1809 – 3 May 1864) was a Cornish plant collector hired by Veitch Nurseries in Exeter, in the neighbouring English county of Devon. His patron James Veitch was a subscriber to the Oregon Botanical Expedition that funded **John Jeffrey**. Lobb met Jeffrey in August 1851 while both were visiting Vancouver Island. He is best known for introducing the monkey puzzle tree (*Araucaria araucana*) commercially to Britain from Chile in the 1840s, and the giant redwood (*Sequoiadendron giganteum*) from California in 1853, which was first named *Wellingtonia gigantia* by **John Lindley** in honour of the Duke of Wellington, who had died the year before.

Scotsman **John Ballenden** (c.1812 – 7 December 1856) was chief factor for the HBC at Fort Vancouver, first meeting John Jeffrey on Vancouver Island in 1851. He later acted as his travelling companion and host during the winters of 1852 and 1853. He married Sarah McLeod (1818–1853), a Métis woman, in 1836 while he was accountant at Upper Fort Garry in the Red River District. During a canoe trip to the west in 1848 he suffered a stroke and temporary paralysis, yet recovered. While he was away on business in 1850, his wife became embroiled in a racially related scandal. Sarah fought to clear her name after being accused of infidelity. The infamous Foss–Pelly case began on 16 July 1850, in which ultimately her accusers were found guilty of defamatory conspiracy, and subsequently dealt hefty fines. Social and racial tensions remained at Red River and, suffering from stress, John Ballenden went on furlough in autumn 1850, afterwards given a new posting to Fort Vancouver. Suffering again from ill health in 1853, John returned to Scotland on furlough a second time when his wife died. On 31 January 1854, he met with **Andrew Murray**, and in a letter to the Oregon Botanical Society the next day, he strongly defended in writing the character of **John Jeffrey**.

Peter Skene Ogden (February 1790 – September 1854) was a fur trader and explorer, first with the North West Company and later with the HBC. In 1816, he was accused of butchering an Indian 'in a most cruel manner', and throughout his career had a reputation for tough negotiation and often violence. Fluent in English and French, he could also converse in several Native American languages. He became famous for saving the lives of 47 settlers after 12 were killed by Cayuse Indians at the Whitman Mission. He was the first white man to explore much of the interior of Oregon, discovering Mount Shasta and the Siskiyou Pass, where a hill is named after him. He rose to the rank of chief factor for the Columbia Department. From Fort Vancouver he corresponded with **Andrew Murray** on two occasions, in December 1853 and May 1854.

Alexander Caulfield Anderson (10 March 1814 – 8 May 1884) was a fur trader with the HBC and explorer of British Columbia. He was the grandson of the Scottish botanist James Anderson (1738–1809). He was chief trader at Fort

Colville when he met **John Jeffrey** in 1851, travelling with him as guide and companion from there to Fort Victoria. His son James Anderson (1841–1930) met John Jeffrey at Fort Colville when 10 years old. Travelling to Edinburgh in 1911, he met the Regius Keeper and shared his story of John Jeffrey shooting a woodpecker.

Charles Sprague Sargent (1841–1927) was the first director of the Arnold Arboretum, serving from his appointment in 1873 for 54 years. At first, there was no arboretum to manage, only the land donated by James Arnold (1781–1868), and he established its offices at Dwight House on his Brookline Estate in Massachusetts. He rose to become the pre-eminent dendrologist of his time, authoring *The Silva of North America* in 14 volumes (1890–1902), and the first two editions of *The Manual of the Trees of North America* (1905 and 1922).

Further Reading

Anderson, A. C. (1872). 'The Dominion at the West: A Brief Description of the Province of British Columbia, its Climate and Resources.' *The Government Prize Essay*, 1872.

Anderson, J. R. (1925). *Trees and Shrubs: Food, Medicinal, and Poisonous Plants of British Columbia*. British Columbia Department of Education.

Anderson, N. (2011). *The Pathfinder: A. C. Anderson's Journeys in the West*. Heritage House Publishing.

Coville, F. V. (1897). 'The Itinerary of John Jeffrey, an Early Botanical Explorer of Western North America.' *Proceedings of the Biological Society of Washington*, 11, 57–60. http://biodiversitylibrary.org/page/2263238

Johnstone, T. J. (1939). 'John Jeffrey and the Oregon Expedition.' *Notes from the Royal Botanic Garden*, Edinburgh, 20: 1–53.

Lang, F. A. (2006). 'John Jeffrey in the Wild West: Speculations on his Life and Times (1828-1854?).' *Kalmiopsis*, 13: 1–12. http://npsoregon.org/kalmiopsis/kalmiopsis13/lang.pdf

Lange, E. F. (1967). 'John Jeffrey and the Oregon Botanical Expedition.' *Oregon Historical Quarterly*. 68, 2: 111–24. http://www.jstor.org/stable/20612972.

Lindsay, A. (2008). *Seeds of Blood and Beauty: Scottish Plant Explorers*. Birlinn Limited.

Morse, W. W. (1969). *Fur Trade Canoe Routes of Canada/ Then and Now*. University of Toronto Press.

Woods, P. and Woods, J. (2003). 'The Oregon Expedition 1850–1854: John Jeffrey and his Conifers.' *Acta Horticulturae*. 615, 289–295. DOI: 10.17660.

Useful Links

The author's website contains a wealth of material featuring the book's creation, plus the latest related news. Additional research is available, including an interactive map which charts precisely John Jeffrey's 10,000-mile expedition route across North America. Visit: www.gabrielhemery.com/books

Other links

American Conifer Society www.conifersociety.org

The Arnold Arboretum of Harvard University www.arboretum.harvard.edu

Hudson's Bay Company archives www.hbcheritage.ca

Nicola Macartney, botanical artist
www.nicolamacartney.com

The Oregon Encyclopedia www.oregonencyclopedia.org

Royal Botanic Garden Edinburgh www.rbge.org.uk

Acknowledgements

This book would have been impossible to write without the enthusiastic co-operation of the Royal Botanic Garden Edinburgh (RBGE). Head of Exhibitions Ian Edwards provided unstinting and enthusiastic support right from the outset of *Green Gold*. He later helped to curate a public exhibition at RBGE which coincided with the book's publication, and which celebrated the life of John Jeffrey. For help in exploring the RBGE archives, I am grateful to Leona Paterson.

It was a privilege to collaborate with Scottish botanical artist Nicola Macartney, whose wonderful illustrations have helped bring the story of John Jeffrey alive, especially during crowdfunding to support publication costs and during the RGBE exhibition.

For assistance with research, I am indebted to Frank Lang, Phil Schapker, Ann Lindsay and Nancy Marguerite Anderson (see www.nancymargueriteanderson.com, and Useful Reading). I am grateful to John Spangler of Antique and Collectable Firearms and Militaria Headquarters (www.oldguns.net) for solving the mystery of the Mississippi Yaeger.

I owe a debt of gratitude to the Unbound team: commissioning editor Xander Cansell; the editorial team of

Josephine Salverda, Laura Gerrard and Gill Harvey, led by Sara Magness; and book designer Mark Ecob.

I could never have completed this book without the love and patience of my family, whose tolerance for my curious writing habits knew no bounds – thank you: Joan, Jane, Ella, Tom and Will.

Finally, as a book whose publication was supported by crowdfunding, I thank all those wonderful people who believed in me. Your names are listed in these pages for all to see.

Unbound is the world's first crowdfunding publisher, established in 2011.

We believe that wonderful things can happen when you clear a path for people who share a passion. That's why we've built a platform that brings together readers and authors to crowdfund books they believe in – and give fresh ideas that don't fit the traditional mould the chance they deserve.

This book is in your hands because readers made it possible. Everyone who pledged their support is listed at the front of the book and below. Join them by visiting unbound.com and supporting a book today.

Richard Mackie
Francesca McLoughlin
Alison Melvin
Nicky Muir
Carlo Navato
James Ogilvie
Pia Ostlund
Clare Owen
Kirsten Parrish

Rich Pigott
Andy Pitman
Keith Rushforth
Claire Scobie
Francesca Shrapnel
Irene Tabb
Carolyn Thorne
Richard Todd
Alun Watkins